*This book is dedicated to you
as a thank you for your interest in* The Archers

INTRODUCTION

With its characters, storylines, humour and coverage of contemporary issues, *The Archers* is drama at its best. And as testament to its quality, it has become the world's longest-running drama serial.

Every week, millions tune in to hear the latest happenings in Ambridge and what the familiar characters are getting up to. It's easy to get caught up in their dilemmas, hopes and tribulations and wonder how it will all work out.

The Archers, which started as 'an everyday story of country folk', is a source of great enjoyment to so many, and this puzzle book aims to continue the joy in those slack moments when the show is off the air. There are special sudokus, anagrams, word searches, criss-crosses, coded crosswords, as well as chances to 'take your pick', deliberate on the meaning of curious country words such as 'tiddle' and 'dumble' and use your skills to decide 'what could possibly go wrong?' There are also rounds of trivia to test your knowledge, which can serve as a reminder of some of the greatest and most humorous moments.

I very much hope you enjoy the puzzles and that, like *The Archers*, this book brings you hours of pleasure and an opportunity to immerse yourself in the special world that is Ambridge.

Good luck and happy puzzling.

Neil Somerville

ANAGRAMS

Unscramble the following to reveal a name and some delightful places where the *Archers* characters live, work and play:

1. THRESH ACRE

2. GAME BIRD

3. SORT BREECH

4. ON THE ROLL

5. AMPLE FRESH

ON TRACK

Enjoy an amble around Ambridge. Starting with the circled letter and moving one letter at a time, either horizontally or vertically, find five well-known buildings.

MYSTERY SUDOKU

Complete the grid so that every row, column and 3 × 3 box contains the letters AFGILMNOR in any order. One row or column contains a seven-letter word connected to Ambridge and *The Archers*. What is it?

O				L	A			M
				F			A	
		G			M	N		
I	F				O			
				G				
			M				N	O
		R	A			I		
	I			R				
L			G	M				R

COUNTRY WORDS

The Archers is set in Borsetshire, which is based on the West Midlands. In this part of the world there are many wonderful country words, but do you know the correct meaning of the following?

1. CATCHING-TIME
  a) Dusk
  b) Heavy shower
  c) Birds about to roost

2. BLOWTH
  a) Pigsty
  b) Blossom
  c) Bundle of straw

3. ROXED
  a) Soft rotten apples or pears
  b) A harvested field
  c) Tree struck by lightning

4. DUMBLE
  a) A forge
  b) A plough
  c) A wooded valley by a stream

HIDDEN NAMES

A character's name is concealed in each of the following sentences. Can you find who is hiding away? As an example, in 'Looking at my long-term career plan, I shall consider every move very carefully', Anisha's name is hidden in the words 'plAN, I SHAll'.

1. Ambridge has a landscape I'll forever admire.

2. To sort this out, I had a meeting place in mind and it's certainly not The Bull.

3. This picture taken at the last Ambridge fete shows us having a really good laugh. Great times. Great memories.

4. Sometimes I indulge in a little wishful thinking. Who doesn't?

CRYPTOGRAM

Solve the cryptogram to discover some wise advice on love given by – who else? – Jazzer. To give you a start, I = B and Q = L.

Solution:

NEVER GIVE YOUR NUMBER

TO A GIRL YOU ARE NOT

INTERESTED IN

WORD SEARCH: THE ARCHERS

In this word search track down the names of some of the Archer family, past and present.

Ben	Jolene
Dan	Josh
David	Kenton
Doris	Laura
Frank	Meriel
Grace	Pat
Helen	Phil
Henry	Pip
Jack	Ruth
Jill	Tom
John	Tony

```
G F P T K C A J X J B Q L S Z
Y I G N N H T R U T H E J L R
P A I H E N Y Y J S M F N I X
C C O L I K X O A Y I O Y I P
F J E V O G S T T K J R T P T
W N K S B H Y T P D E X O A S
O N N J L N B R S A A N P D L
A A A I O S J W M E H N T R A
E S R T A G N O L U U R A O D
C R F V Y H T E L L A U R A N
A K A V G O I F X E K D L V D
R T F C G R M P M X N U L H A
G A E B E O H E N R Y E I E V
K X X M D Y S J N W O F J Q I
N F Z L I H P E S T F N U H D
```

AN ARCHERS RIDDLE

My first is in Lynda but not in Snell,
My second is in water but not in well.
My third is in fine but not in coarse,
My fourth is in shire and also in horse.
My fifth is in penny but not in Hassett,
And my whole is certainly, to Helen,
A real asset.

What am I?

TRIVIA:
PAST AND PRESENT

Dig deep into your Ambridge memories – can you answer these fiendish questions?

1. Who was born in a tent at the Glastonbury Festival in 1998?

2. What is the name of the draught beer served at The Bull?

3. Under what name has Lynda Snell written for *The Borchester Life*?

4. What sort of animals were Mrs Archer, Noah, Mrs Noah and Romeo? Who owned them?

5. What was the name of the pub that closed its doors in Ambridge?

6. Before his trial in early 2019, Brian was determined to plead not guilty and 'have his day in court.' However, he changed his mind after talking and listening to which venerable villager?

7. What major and slightly questionable prop went missing in the 2018 production of *The Canterbury Tales*?

8. Who set up a gnome-making enterprise?

9. How did Helen and Tom's brother John die?

10. Who currently lives at Honeysuckle Cottage?

CROSSWORD

Across

6 Once a Larkin, now a Grundy (7)

7 Initially declared a victory in diversifying at Brookfield (5)

9 Mr Crawford (4)

10 Cathedral city, sixteen miles from Ambridge (10)

11 Joins, as long-lost friends (8)

13 Provoke (6)

15 Church recess (4)

17 Wading bird (5)

18 Irritation (4)

19 Alice's relation to Pip (6)

20 Siege (8)

23 Short-legged dog (5, 5)

26 Pig farmer's confused line (4)

27 Am (5)

28 Favourite haunt of many, including some ghosts (3, 4)

Down

1 Servers at 28A (10)

2 What the businesses in Ambridge look for (6)

3 Tolled at St Stephen's (4)

4 Attachment, sticking together (8)

5 Nights before (4)

6 Pursue (5)

8 Extreme (7)

12 Plant seen in many an Ambridge garden (5)

14 Where fowls are kept (7, 3)

16 Innovator (7)

17 Barrow pushed by person (8)

21 A sterling hunter (6)

22 Seed device. Boring? (5)

24 Set aside (4)

25 Within the Archer family, she's really truthful (4)

A PERPLEXING POSER

Over the years Jill Archer has experienced many joys as well as dealt with personal tragedy. She has proved a strong, resilient and redoubtable figure who has contributed much to Ambridge life. But could it be that Jill also knows how to predict the future? And if not, how was it that she knew about the birth of her third granddaughter before she was even born?

WEDDING BELLS

Wedding bells have often rung out across Ambridge. Put the following weddings in the order they occurred, with the earliest first.

a) Jolene Rogers and Sid Perks

b) Grace Fairbrother and Phil Archer

c) Caroline Pemberton and Oliver Sterling

d) Nic Hanson and Will Grundy

e) Shula Archer and Mark Hebden

f) Hayley Jordan and Roy Tucker

g) Elizabeth Archer and Nigel Pargetter

h) Ian Craig and Adam Macy

i) Lilian Nicholson and Ralph Bellamy

j) Emma Carter and William Grundy

AMBRIDGE SUDOKU

Time to puzzle and ponder over Ambridge, the centre of all that happens in *The Archers*. In this special sudoku, complete the grid so that every column and 2 × 4 box contains the letters that make up the name 'Ambridge'.

D	B				G		
A					D		B
			R	E	B		
		G					
						G	
	I	M		A			
			A	M			I
	R						E

WHAT COULD POSSIBLY GO WRONG?

1. Walter Gabriel frequently visited Dan and Doris at Brookfield Farm and sometimes lent a hand in the kitchen. However, what went wrong?
    a) When helping Doris prepare Sunday lunch, Walter mistook the sugar for salt, which made the meal inedible. Doris, who had invited some guests she wished to impress, was not best pleased.
    b) Walter let the soup boil over, making a mess of Doris's new cooker. It took a lot of effort to clean.
    c) Trying to help with the washing up, Walter scoured Doris's saucepans and, in the process, removed their non-stick coating.

2. Why was the photograph that Lynda Snell entered into the 2008 Flower and Produce Show disqualified?
    a) It was a picture taken at Waterley Cross and not of Ambridge, which the rules stipulated.
    b) The photo submitted exceeded the permitted size by half an inch.
    c) The photo had been digitally manipulated.

WORD QUEST: KENTON

Whether serving in the Merchant Navy, selling antiques or revitalising The Bull, Kenton has shown himself to be a man of many talents, although he has also experienced a few disasters as well. In this word quest, make as many words as you can with three or more letters out of his name.

KENTON

16 words = excellent
13 words = very good
8 words = good
3 words = better luck next time!

WORD LADDER

Pig farming is a big industry in Ambridge. In this word ladder change one letter at a time to turn – or lead a – 'pig' into 'sty'.

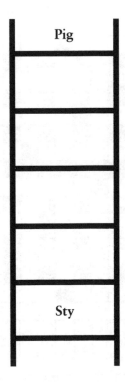

Pig

Sty

CODED CROSSWORD

Each letter of the alphabet has been replaced by a number. To solve the puzzle, you must decide which letter is represented by which number. To help you start, one of the words has been partly filled in. When you have solved the code, complete the bottom grid to discover the name of something familiar. What is it?

FAMOUS MOMENTS

Ambridge might be sleepy, but every so often it gets its moment in the spotlight. Can you remember these brushes with fame?

1. Who is well known for his rhyming couplets and reciting old country lore and was even invited to appear on the regional television show *In Your Corner*?
2. Who led the indie band Little White Lies on a national tour in 2008?
3. In what capacity did Dame Eileen Atkins, Nigel Havers and Catherine Tate all appear in an *Archers* episode broadcast in 2016?
4. Which famous mystery writer visited Ambridge in 2010 to open Lynda Snell's Whodunnit-themed village fete?
5. In 1988, who enjoyed a lively exchange with Dame Edna Everage at the Birmingham Hippodrome?
6. Which famed broadcaster called in at Grey Gables in 1989 to play in Jack Woolley's celebrity golfing weekend?
7. Which celebrity helped with a village hall fundraising challenge in 1993, and returned in 2016 to celebrate the reopening of the hall after flood damage?
8. Which member of the royal family made a visit to Ambridge in 1984 and so became the first royal to play a part in a BBC drama programme?
9. Which member of the royal family appeared in the sixtieth anniversary episode of *The Archers* in 2011?
10. Which celebrated actress played the part of Pru Forrest for the show's 10,000th episode in 1989?

ANAGRAMS

Unscramble the following to reveal some well-known Ambridge names.

1. LAND BRIGADIER

2. RARE CLIENT

3. BORN TELLERS

4. MAKE A NEAT KID

5. OR REMATCH?

MYSTERY SUDOKU

Complete the grid so that every row, column and 3 × 3 box contains the letters BCEHIMNOT in any order. One row or column contains a seven-letter word that could be useful to farmers in Ambridge. What is it?

O		I						
			C	T		I	O	
		C				T		E
C		N	O					
			E		N			
				B	H			O
T		H				N		
	I	B		E	M			
						M		I

WHAT THEY SAID

1. This was a favourite saying of the redoubtable Mrs Perkins (Peggy Woolley's mother), but how did it end?

   'There's a price to be paid for everything in this life.
   _____ *'*

           a) And housework is one of them.
           b) So always pay your dues.
           c) Especially if it shaves.

2. What did Dan Archer think?

   *'*_____ *has a great bearing on a marriage.'*
           a) Good cooking
           b) Central heating
           c) Laughter

3. A saying from Walter Gabriel's Granny:

   'A farmer who won't help a friend when he ought,
   will finish his days _____ *'*
           a) with nought.
           b) in the bankruptcy court.
           c) miserable and fraught.

WORD BUILDER

The letters of a nine-letter word have been numbered one to nine. Solve the clues to discover something much admired about Ambridge.

Letters 4, 7 and 3 give us a Hedben Lloyd.

Letters 6, 2 and 8 give us a hat.

Letters 1, 7, 3 and 9 give us a country road.

Letters 5, 8, 2, 4 and 9 give us a gardening tool.

Letters 5, 6, 2, 1 and 9 give us a measure.

1	2	3	4	5	6	7	8	9

NAME JIG

The names of five characters have been cut up into sections. Join the pieces together to see who they are.

ER NDY ZA RID GET

NIF OLI HEL

ED

BETH PAR TER

VER JEN

LING ARC

STER

ALD GE

HER GRU

DIE EN ELI

COUNTRY WORDS

There are many wonderful country words, but do you know the correct meaning of the following, all of which come from the Midlands, aka Borsetshire?

1. COSH
a) Marsh
b) Sharp shower
c) Pods of peas or beans

2. DROCK
a) A young hen
b) A drain or ditch
c) To cut back a hedge

3. YUCKEL
a) The green woodpecker
b) A barren cow
c) Shallow tub

4. MAURS
a) Larder or cool storage room
b) Marsh marigold
c) Tree roots

MINI SUDOKU: GRUNDY

The Grundys, with their tenacity, enterprise and aspirations, bring much joy and also some poignancy to life in Ambridge. In this mini sudoku, glory in the Grundy name so that every row, column and 2 × 3 box contains the letters of the name 'Grundy'.

N			D		
		G		U	
	R			Y	
	Y	R			
G					

TAKE YOUR PICK

Which of the following is the correct answer? Take your pick.

1. Nigel Pargetter had many jobs but at one time he sold what?
   a) Encyclopaedias
   b) Swimming pools
   c) Conservatories

2. Walter Gabriel arranged many money-making attractions for the Ambridge Fete but one of the most popular and successful was Marmaduke. What was Marmaduke?
   a) A vintage steam engine
   b) A ventriloquist's dummy
   c) A dappled pony who pulled a trap around the fete grounds and village

3. Richard Adamson was a major figure in Ambridge for much of the 1970s and 1980s. What was his job?
   a) Vicar
   b) Vet
   c) Solicitor

4. Martha Woodford was a keen knitter and over the years knitted what for the village children?
   a) Hats
   b) Scarves
   c) Cardigans

WORD SEARCH:
THE COUNTRYSIDE

In this word search, enjoy the sights of the countryside as you seek out the following.

Barley	Herd
Barn	Horse
Bull	Lamb
Calf	Mare
Cockerel	Meadow
Ewe	Paddock
Farmhouse	Pig
Goat	Plough
Haystack	Sheep
Hedge	Stable
Heifer	Tractor

```
L R A J Q E E C T P P E M L Q
E G O A T P S P M I Q S V G S
R E L B M E L U S G Y R P J L
E N A A M B L O O F I O X F R
K N M G L B G B U H L H V A E
C E B V A W D A A G M F Y P F
O N Q R M U P R S T H R G N I
C A L E M A V N H M S L A F E
K E P I D W E T E F L A C F H
Y G M D O T R I E Q A B I H K
Q Q O D E A R K P L U T E C N
Z C A G C E M J I L V R H O G
K E D T Z R E K L N D I S B E
M E O X Q A K C A T S Y A H W
H R Y T L M L U G U A T T E E
```

CRYPTOGRAM

Solve the cryptogram to reveal one of Tom Forrest's seasonal observations. To give you a start, I = L, F = W and N = A.

D	B	M		M	H	J	I	A	R	B		F	A	H	D	M	C
							L					W					

–		M	H	K	A	H	J		A	H		U	E	I	O,		D	Q
–														L	,			

C	M	Z	Q	Y	Y	M	H	Z	M		A	H		N	E	J	E	R	D
														A					

MAZE

For several years Home Farm featured a maze, including a Magi-maze with a Harry Potter theme and a Dino-maze promising a 'mammoth' experience. Here's a chance to enjoy a maze, although maybe not a maize maze, as you find your way from start to finish.

START

FINISH

TRIVIA: NAMES

Ambridge certainly has its share of unusual names. Here's a chance to test your knowledge of them.

1. Whose middle name is Peregrine?

2. What is Jolene's real name?

3. Who was named after one of the characters in *Dynasty*, a popular 1980s TV series?

4. What was Matt Crawford's nickname for Lilian?

5. Who were Bunty and Reg?

6. Who once owned (and later ate) a pet turkey called Bathsheba?

7. What was the name of Rob Titchener's first wife?

8. What are the names of Robert Snell's two daughters from his first marriage?

9. When one of Robert Snell's daughters had a son, they caused Lynda considerable anguish by nearly calling the boy Mowgli. What did they call him instead?

10. What building had once been called Onemomona?

31

ONE FROM THE OTHER

A name and something connected with that name have been blended together. Separate one and find the other.

HHEORBAMLEFLAERYSM

CRISS-CROSS: AMBRIDGE RESIDENTS

Fit all these residents, past and present, into the grid.

3-letter names
Jim
Rex
Tom

4-letter names
Adam
Alan
Emma
Jill
Josh
Mike
Neil
Tony
Usha

5-letter names
Brian
David
Helen

Lynda
Peggy

6-letter names
Hayley
Jolene
Justin
Kenton
Kirsty
Oliver
Phoebe
Ruairi

7-letter name
Clarrie

8-letter names
Alistair
Harrison
Jennifer

FOLLOW THE LEADER

The names of three well-known characters have been jumbled together and entered below. The letters of the names are in the order in which they appear reading anti-clockwise. Starting from the N, bottom right, discover who they are.

A	R	C	L	G	I	I
P						D
U		Y	R	E		P
R		R		H		E
A				D		E
N	R	T	C	E		N

VERY STRANGE BUT TRUE

At one time Joe Grundy led ghost walks around the village telling tales of hauntings, including that of the Little Drummer Boy at The Bull. In the 1980s, the young Lucy Perks was not at all keen on her new bedroom situated above the pub. It was cold and she heard strange noises... could it be the Drummer Boy? The next day her father Sid listened and, to his alarm, he too heard noises. A ghost hunter from Waterley Cross was called in to investigate, but what caused the noises?

a) A bird had nested in the loft

b) Air locks in the antiquated plumbing system

c) A loose TV aerial

d) The sporadic reverberation of a refrigeration unit under the bedroom

e) The source of the noise was never discovered, leaving everyone on edge for quite some time. However, the ghost hunter did bring some welcome publicity (and extra custom) for The Bull, which pleased Sid.

BETWEEN THE LINES

Elizabeth Pargetter, Josh Archer, Brian Aldridge, Robert Snell – this word applies to them all, as well as to others who live in Ambridge. And this word can be inserted into the blank line below so that, reading downward, nine three-letter words can be formed. What is the word hidden between the lines?

I	H	A	P	D	A	D	O	U
Y	D	P	Y	D	E	N	E	E

MYSTERY SUDOKU

Complete the grid so that every row, column and 3 × 3 box contains the letters CEIKLOSTV in any order. One row or column contains a nine-letter word that is something important for the Ambridge economy. What is it?

	T		V	E				C
E	K	C		L		S		
		I					K	
					E			
I	V			T			L	O
		O						
	I					O		
		K		O		V	E	I
C				K	V		S	

TRUE DIAMONDS

Hidden in each diamond is a familiar name or place, written in either a clockwise or anti-clockwise direction. What are they?

1.

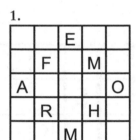

2.

		I		
	D		R	
G				D
	E		L	
		A		

3.

		R		
	R		I	
A				S
	H		O	
		N		

4.

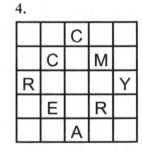

A FARMING RIDDLE

My first is in Archer but not in Pargetter
And my second is also in Archer but not in Perks.
My third is in Pargetter but not in Archer,
And so is my fourth.
My fifth is in Neil but not in Carter,
While my sixth is in both Neil and Carter.
My whole you will see in many a field,
For I give to Ambridge quite a yield.

What am I?

CODED CROSSWORD

Each letter of the alphabet has been replaced by a number. To solve the puzzle, you must decide which letter is represented by which number. To help you start, one of the words has been partly filled in. When you have solved the code, complete the bottom grid to discover a name. What and where is it?

	7		21		24				7		24		1	
7	13	25	9	6	13	20	18		10	3	7	25	7	11
	13		14		3		9		7		9		12	
22	7	17	17		7	8	7	16	13	10	7	3	12	6
	18				15		3		6		11		26	
24	4	6	13	18	25		3	6	24	6	7	3	18	25
			3		7		20				16		4	
		18	7	13	13	9	6	10	3	20	12	24		
	24		12				10		26		6			
9	20	18	6	16	24	6	3		18	14	3	13	24	23
	19		11		26		14		4				7	
3	6	1	7	23	11	6	16	13	24		15	20	9	9
	24		3		5		12		13		6		11	
2	14	7	4	6	3		23	6	7	3	5	26	26	4
	1		24		6				3		24		16	

Row8: L E G under 7 6 10

1	2	3	4	5	6 E	7	8	9	10 G	11	12	13
14	15	16	17	18	19	20	21	22	23	24	25	26

(L under 9)

| 14 | 16 | 12 | 6 | 3 | 15 | 26 | 26 | 12 | 24 |

ANAGRAMS

Unscramble the following to reveal some well-known names.

1. RECURRING LADY

2. VARIED CHARD

3. A SCARE TURNS

4. REGRET DEFIED PART

5. OK TRY CURE

CROSSWORD

Across

1 Time to come (6)
4 Fruit (6)
9 Shires (4)
10 Organic centre (6, 4)
11 Weather map line (6)
12 Fallon is quite an accomplished one (8)
13 Popular beauty spot (5, 4)
15 Ambridge gamekeeper (4)
16 Earth (4)
17 Mechanical equipment seen in many parts of Ambridge (9)
22 Sentimental (8)
23 Siobhan's son (6)
25 A favourite food of Helen's (4, 6)
26 Smudge (4)
27 Employ again (6)
28 Colourless gas (6)

Down

1 Fragrant flower (7)
2 Pulsate (5)
3 Renaissance (7)
5 Month (6)
6 Fondness (9)
7 Overseas post (7)
8 Gloomy (6)
14 Formerly Ms Snowy (9)
16 Plot discloser (7)
18 Dan, Doris, Phil ... (6)
19 Crop (7)
20 Send a different way (7)
21 Engraver (6)
24 Hayley and Roy's daughter (5)

COUNTRY WORDS

There are many wonderful country words but do you know the correct meaning of the following? They all come from the Midlands, aka Borsetshire.

1. COTT
a) Fleece of an old ewe
b) Drinking trough
c) Stubble left after harvest

2. TWINTER
a) The weakest of a flock
b) A clear, starry night
c) A two-year-old sheep

3. BROWSE
a) Brushwood
b) Small bucket
c) Animal shelter

4. TIDDLE
a) Hand-grips of a scythe
b) To rear an animal by hand
c) Weeding hoe

LETTER DROP

The letters in each of the columns need to be entered into the squares immediately below, but not necessarily in the same order. By placing the letters in the correct places you will reveal some thoughts of Mary Pound, at one time an active figure in Ambridge, not least as a member of the ladies' football team.

	S							
	I	O	K	E		O	H	
	I	G	R	G	Y	S	B	
S	A	L	T	L	O	T	O	
M	H	B	U	A	S	O	U	E
T	A	N	L	E	D	T	D	E

TAKE YOUR PICK

Which of the following is the correct answer? Take your pick.

1. What bit a young Adam Macy in 1977?
   a) An adder
   b) A rat
   c) A dog

2. Freda Fry was for many years the cook at The Bull, but on one occasion how did she hurt herself?
   a) She dropped a rolling pin on her foot
   b) She dropped hot tomato soup on her foot, not only scalding her but causing panic when Kenton thought it was blood
   c) She dropped a large frozen lasagne on her foot

3. When Lynda Snell decided to introduce Feng Shui to Ambridge Hall, why did she remove Robert's Turkish rug from the hall?
   a) It was the wrong shape
   b) It was too brown
   c) She wanted to 'create space' and regarded the rug as 'clutter'

4. What did Fallon Rogers find in her garden the morning after her hen party?
   a) A garden gnome
   b) A road sign
   c) A llama

NAME BUILDER

The letters of a nine-letter name have been numbered one to nine. Solve the clues to discover what the name is – it's one that has had quite an impact on the lives of many in Ambridge.

Letters 4, 5 and 9 give us the name of
one of the younger Archers

Letters 3, 8, 6 and 2 give us something additional

Letters 6, 8, 4 and 2 give us a gown

Letters 1, 8 and 7 give us a container

Letters 4, 8, 9 and 5 give us a type of china

Letters 7, 5, 3, 1, 2 and 6 give us an angry state of mind

And letters 8, 3, 5 and 9 give us a sign
that perhaps all is not good

1	2	3	4	5	6	7	8	9

CRISS-CROSS: AMBRIDGE

Ambridge got its name through being a crossing point over the River Am. A surprising number of words can be made out of the letters in Ambridge and the following are just some of them. Fit them all into the grid.

3-letter words
Aim
Bar
Era

4-letter words
Amid
Beam
Bird
Bred
Dame
Dear
Game
Gram
Idea
Mead
Read

5-letter words
Braid
Grade
Image
Media

6-letter words
Admire
Badger
Mirage

7-letter words
Abridge
Brigade

TRIVIA: TIMES PAST AND PRESENT

Here's some trivia of things that are not always trivial. See how you get on.

1. In November 2018, what product did Tom decide would no longer be made, much to Susan's concern?

2. Matt was badly injured in a hit-and-run accident on the night of the Hunt Ball. There was much speculation about the driver involved. Who did it turn out to be?

3. In the Highland Games held at the village fete in 2013, what were tossed instead of cabers?

4. Who is the karate instructor in Ambridge?

5. Who did a runner to Costa Rica?

6. When there was a promises auction held in aid of church funds, who had the temerity to suggest that Lynda Snell should 'promise to mind her own business for a week?'

7. What sort of robotic picker did Alice want to trial at Home Farm?

8. Where in Ambridge is a ha-ha?

9. In the 2018 production of *The Canterbury Tales*, who was voted the best teller?

10. And what was the prize the best teller won?

MYSTERY SUDOKU

Complete the grid so that every row, column and 3 × 3 box contains the letters AEIMNPRST in any order. One row or column contains a nine-letter name. What is it and to whom does it belong?

	E						P	
P			N					R
	N	S			P		M	
			A					T
		N	I		T	S		
R					N			
	I		M			N	T	
E					A			P
	S						E	

CROSS OUT

Cross out all the letters that appear more than once. The letters that are left, reading from top to bottom and left to right, will spell out a name or word related to *The Archers*. Who or what is it?

P	S	B	F	L	A	M	V
C	I	W	T	H	X	J	Q
Z	P	O	M	K	I	C	E
H	G	L	V	B	R	F	A
S	X	I	U	L	A	N	K
B	D	Z	W	Y	M	Q	T

HIDDEN NAMES

A character's name is hidden in each of the following sentences. Can you uncover them?

1. After leaving school, I very much fancied joining the military.

2. I hated being in a rut. However, recent developments have opened up new possibilities.

3. In my business I have to look at every aspect, including all the many regulations.

4. To lose that extra weight I guess I need dietary advice on what best to avoid.

CRYPTOGRAM

Solve the cryptogram to discover some advice Jolene once gave to Kenton. To give you a start, F = Y and B = W.

N	Z	U	F		K	R		V	N	K		E	R	K	X	W	E	V		B	G	R	E	V
			Y																	W				

W	J		F	R	C		E	N	S	N	G		Q	R		E	R	K	X	W	E	V
			Y																			

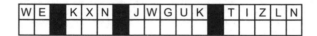

W	E		K	X	N		J	W	G	U	K		T	I	Z	L	N

NAME JIG

The names of five characters have been cut up into sections. Join the pieces together to see who they are.

KAT

LEY

YD

KS

LYN

DA

ALIS

HY

HAY

LLO

SNE

PER

TUC

HER

JO

ARC

TAIR

KER

LL

SH

WORD SEARCH: ANIMALS

Animals and pets play an important part in the life of Ambridge. See if you can track down all the following.

Benjamin
Bess
Captain
Constanza
Daphne
Demeter
Eccles
Judy
Maisie
Midnight

Mitch
Nell
Portia
Salieri
Scruff
Timus
Tolly
Tootsie
Turpin

```
B N T Q B H A U E H C T I M E
Y E R H A I T R O P N Y V T E
M T N K G R X U P I K Q D M B
Q I E J B I I R E I L A S U W
N M A I A E N X W L K S C U J
H U Q Q I M Y D L M W P R U I
R S N S G C I N I H P F U E E
B J I O Q L G N C M U Y F C E
R A F B L H R T P A E S F C N
M I A E P S T B I L P Y Q L H
P U N D E M E T E R L T Z E P
E I S T O O T O O L H D A S A
Z S S E B S D X O D I T P I D
M W N I P R U T R K C X M U N
M L N C O N S T A N Z A F G V
```

WORD BUILDER

The letters of a nine-letter word have been numbered 1 to 9. Solve the clues to discover a particular home valued in Ambridge.

Letters 2, 8 and 6 give us a senior Archer

Letters 4, 7, 1 and 6 give us corrosion

Letters 2, 8, 5 and 9 give us a bucket

Letters 2, 9, 7 and 1 give us +

Letters 6, 4, 3, and 2 cause us to stumble

Letters 5, 4, 3 and 1 give us a spring flower

1	2	3	4	5	6	7	8	9

MINI SUDOKU: SILAGE

With so much livestock in Ambridge, an eye has to be kept on silage levels, especially in winter months. Because of the 2018 heatwave, silage levels in early 2019 got particularly low. In this mini sudoku, complete the grid so that every row, column and 2 × 3 box contains the letters that make up the word 'silage'.

	I		L		A
				G	
S					
	E				L
	L	I			G

WHAT COULD POSSIBLY GO WRONG?

1. In a game of Murder held at Lower Loxley Hall in 2002, what went wrong?
   a) Lynda Snell dressed up a mannequin to create a body. However, her creation was so realistic that Elizabeth fainted and several others were led away screaming.
   b) Robert Snell had agreed to be the body but needed to use the bathroom, so the body went missing at the crucial time.
   c) Kenton spilled fake blood on one of Lower Loxley's antique silk carpets.

2. In the 'Three Peaks Challenge' held in 2003, the course was completed in fancy dress. Lynda Snell dressed up as a Fabergé egg but what was the unanticipated consequence?
   a) During the race Lynda fell and, because of her round costume, could not get back on her feet. In the end several people had to come to her rescue and haul her upright, which left Lynda feeling very embarrassed.
   b) Lynda got stuck in the church tower and had to be cut out of her costume.
   c) The frame of the costume got dented, which gave Lynda some unexpected and extenuated curves.

ARCHERS HIDE AND SEEK

Archers are hiding somewhere in the grid and they only appear once. Can you find them?

```
A R H A E A C S E R S H A C H
R R C R E S R A C R A R C H S
A S H R C A H S E R S E H S A
C R C R S C R A H A S H R E R
E S A R E C A C E R C E H R A
A R H R C E H R E S R E S R S
S R R R C C A C H C S E R C H
A E S H E C R S E A R S H E A
C S H R S A C S S C S E H R C
A S R A E C R S E A E A C E A
R R C R E C R C E R S E H R S
A A H A S C A R H A H E C A E
S A S C E H R S E E S E H S R
A R E A S C A H E A R A R A A
C A R A E C H S E R S S H C A
```

ANAGRAMS

Unscramble the following to reveal some well-known characters' names.

1. ALL SOLIDARITY

2. NORTHERN CAKE

3. WELL I'M A RICH CASE

4. ALERT GIRL TYPE

5. FIX RARE HERB ROT

TRUE OR FALSE?

Decide whether the following statements are true or false. They all relate to St Stephen's Church.

1. There is a memorial window in St Stephen's commemorating Grace Archer.

2. Before he was ordained, Alan Franks was a PE teacher.

3. Rosalind Fisher was a former vicar.

4. In the great storm of 1987 the weather vane got damaged and, until it was repaired, was stuck pointing in an easterly direction.

5. Will Grundy had a narrow escape when some clock weights crashed to the floor.

6. The poet John Betjeman wrote a poem called 'St Stephen's of Ambridge'.

7. Eddie Grundy was once caught metal detecting in the church yard looking for old sovereigns.

8. In a robbery in 1996 the carved Bishop's Chair was stolen.

9. In 2007 Alan Franks abseiled from the church tower to raise money for charity.

CRISS-CROSS

Over the years, quite a few ponies and horses have been mentioned in *The Archers*. Fit them all into the grid.

4-letter names
Duff
Ippy
Ivor

5-letter names
Basil
Boxer
Comet
Fleur
Minty
Pluto
Tolly

6-letter names
Colfax
Magnet
Maisie

Nimrod
Silver

7-letter names
Blossom
Maxwell
Tootsie

8-letter names
Bartleby
Chandler
Grey Silk
Midnight

9-letter names
Red Knight
Spearmint
Sylvester

LETTER DROP

The letters in each of the columns need to be entered into the squares immediately below, but not necessarily in the same order. By placing the letters in the correct places you will reveal words said by Ian Craig.

			O	H				
	E	C	W	S				
U	T	E	I	U	L	H		
V	M	H	I	I	O	D		
O	W	H	T	S	T	N		
S	I	P	N	I	P	I	N	G

COUNTRY WORDS

Do you know the correct meaning of these lovely country words, all of which come from the Midlands, aka Borsetshire?

1. CHILVER
a) Peal of bells
b) Larder or cold storage room
c) Ewe lamb

2. SUFFING
a) Digging drains
b) Type of thatch
c) Passing shower

3. CONGER
a) Cucumber
b) Corn cob
c) Fishing net

4. STELCH
a) Marshy area
b) Leather strap fitted to the leg of
a falcon
c) A post in the cattle stall

WORD LADDER

The milk from cows is a valuable commodity in Ambridge, used in the making of many dairy products. In this word ladder, here's a chance to get milk from cows. Change one letter at a time to turn the word 'cows' into 'milk'.

Cows

Milk

A PICTURE POSER

What place is suggested by the following and why was this so significant in 2016?

CODED CROSSWORD

Each letter of the alphabet has been replaced by a number. To solve the puzzle, you must decide which letter is represented by which number. To help you start, one of the words has been partly filled in. When you have solved the code, complete the bottom grid to discover the name of somewhere special in Ambridge. What and where is it?

1	2	3 M	4	5	6	7	8 T	9	10	11 E	12	13
14	15	16	17	18	19	20	21	22	23	24	25	26

5	18	19	25	26	11	18	23

HIDDEN CHARMS

Solve the clues and two words will be formed in the shaded squares. This is what many visitors often see and appreciate when they come to Ambridge.

1. Salad plant

2. Rabbit home

3. Sequence

4. Type of owl

5. Senior

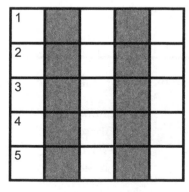

WORD SEARCH: NAMES

```
M W A M M E Q T M L G E C O L
B A E Q D D X R I A T S I L A
X J D M J D K T P E B E O H P
H G O A Q D A V I D W L I E N
A N Z R P B X J A S H L E T N
K Q Q Z R R A Y E J L J E I V
T Z O I P E G G Y N T H O R A
I H A R R I S O N G N C C L H
B N I R I A U R O M T I A B L
T L R C C A E R K W F N F X J
Y Y P Q K N S R J W X P B E Q
N G H N E C L A R R I E F G R
O F X L K D X T T U R L L I J
T C O Q H E L E N A D N Y L A
Q J T V P H B W U S U O G M K
```

Have a look round the grid to find all these familiar names.

Adam	Emma	Lynda
Alan	Harrison	Neil
Alistair	Helen	Peggy
Brian	Jennifer	Phoebe
Clarrie	Jill	Ruairi
David	Jolene	Tony

TRIVIA: TIMES GONE BY

Can you recall these memorable moments in Ambridge?

1. What did David once shoot in a fit of rage?
2. Why was Rob Titchener keen to pay off Stefan?
3. How long was the sentence Susan received after she was found guilty of harbouring her fugitive brother Clive?
4. The Single Wicket competition is held in memory of whom?
5. Which well-known gardener judged Ambridge's entries in the National Gardens Scheme open gardens competition in May 2003?
6. Which character used to lament, 'Nobody cares about poor old...'?
7. As well as Ambridge, the vicar, Alan Franks, looks after three other parishes. Edgeley and Darrington are two of them, but what is the third?
8. In one memorable episode who shared a shower with whom?
9. Following the 2015 production of *Calendar Girls*, a calendar was produced. However, who was concerned that too much of them was showing and insisted on star-shaped stickers to cover up certain bits?
10. Which county does Ruth come from?

INTERESTING PUZZLE

Match the character to their interest.

1.	Philip	a)	cats
2.	Henry	b)	upcycling
3.	Neil	c)	classic tractors
4.	Fallon	d)	crosswords
5.	Peggy	e)	bird watching
6.	Bert	f)	bee-keeping
7.	Kate	g)	singing
8.	Tony	h)	composing verse
9.	Alan	i)	vegan food
10.	Jolene	j)	karate
11.	Christine	k)	motorbikes
12.	Jill	l)	bell ringing

WORD BUILDER

The letters of a nine-letter word have been numbered 1 to 9. Solve the clues to discover something that is very much a feature of Ambridge and its residents.

Letters 7, 1 and 9 give us very cold conditions

Letters 8, 2, 6 and 9 give us a senior Archer

Letters 3, 7, 6 and 8 give us a herb

Letters 2, 4, 7 and 8 give us something to leave out

Letters 1, 5, 3, 7 and 6 give us an aromatic spice

Letters 8, 2, 6, 7 and 1 give us a pick-me-up

1	2	3	4	5	6	7	8	9

WORD SEARCH: FIELD NAMES

The following are the names of some of the fields at Bridge Farm and Brookfield. Can you do some fieldwork by finding them all in the grid?

Ashfield	Low Field
Ashmead	Lower Parks
Big Leys	Marney's
Burntland	Oakey Bank
Coombebell	Six Acre
Far Pasture	Skipperley
Home Field	Tarbutts
Kingcups	The Dell
Lakey Hill	Trefoil
Long Meadow	Wormitts

```
G F S E W L L I H Y E K A L S A Y
A I T F S T T U B R A T A I Y X R
L S T U H L Q N U J S P S R E F B
O J I S T R A T V T K Q H G N W H
N L M Z N H S S X L I O F E R T O
G F R I C A E G H K P K I G A V M
M P O Y P B K D D M P F E L M U E
E S W R K I H N E I E Y L L O S F
A D A G E G A N C L R A D E W K I
D F A Z W L U Q C V L S D B W R E
O M D P T E V I B P E N T E I A L
W E X N J Y O C U V Y Q D B P P D
B J R Q H S P U C G N I K M U R E
Y U K J N E R C A X I S I O I E G
B D K C G N X V D G P S D O X W A
Q L O R S D L E I F W O L C Z O N
D E K N A B Y E K A O C T T O L Z
```

WHAT COULD POSSIBLY GO WRONG?

1. In 1987, Ambridge made it to the finals of the Best-Kept Village competition and were competing against Loxley Barrett. However, Ambridge was to miss out, with some suspecting skulduggery from Loxley Barrett residents. What went wrong?
   a) Just prior to judging, a scarecrow wearing a bikini was put on the village green.
   b) A pile of beer cans were found dumped in the village pond.
   c) A map and information sheet outside the village hall (for the benefit of the judges) had been turned upside down.

2. When Marjorie Antrobus decided to have a beech tree felled, what was the unexpected consequence?
   a) The beech tree fell on her greenhouse.
   b) The contractor carrying out the work developed a crush on her and for several months sent her bouquets of red roses.
   c) As the beech tree was removed some human bones were found. These dated from Victorian times and greatly disturbed Marjorie but delighted Joe Grundy, who included the site of the tree in his Ambridge Ghost Walk.

ACROSTICS

Solve the clues correctly and an important business will be revealed in the shaded squares. What is it?

1. Greek sun god
2. Feeding trough
3. Be part of
4. Part of eye
5. Apprentice
6. Site of Greek oracle
7. Pungent bulb
8. Peacock at The Bull

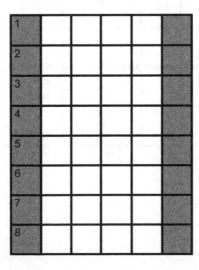

MINI SUDOKU: VEG BOX

The Veg Box has been a great success at Bridge Farm. This mini sudoku gives you the chance to fill the empty boxes in the grid so that every row, column and 2 × 3 box contains the letters that make up 'Veg Box'.

			V		
	O			G	
	B	E		V	
O					
				E	
X					

HIDDEN NAMES

A character's name has been smuggled in to each of the following sentences. Who is hiding there?

1. I like playing in Ambridge or getting out in the open countryside.

2. This lady has aspirations of one day being seen at a shareholders' meeting.

3. If it's a case of being more frugal, I certainly can cut down on the food bill.

4. My new housekeeping system makes sense, seeing as how we have to economise now.

MIND THE GAP

Each of the following words is missing a letter. Put the missing letter into the grid below to reveal a place where you might need to mind the gap!

1. _atch

2. St_le

3. _atch

4. S_eet

5. B_nds

6. Ca_ed

7. _ight

8. R_cks

9. S_are

1	2	3	4	5	6	7	8	9

CRYPTOGRAM

Solve the cryptogram to discover these rather rueful words from Alistair. To give you a start, Q = L and M = W.

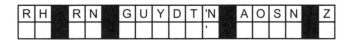

RH RN GUYDT'N AOSN Z
(IF IT DOESN'T HURT A)

QRNNQY MAYT CUO QUDY,
(LITTLE WHEN YOU LOSE,)

NAYSY'D TU WURTN RT
(THERE'S NO POINT IN)

WQZCRTE
(PLAYING)

WORD SEARCH: LOVE STORIES

Ambridge has witnessed a great many love stories, including some of the following. Seek these out in this romantic heart.

Adam	Mark
Alan	Natasha
David	Nigel
Elizabeth	Pat
Fallon	Peggy
Harrison	Philip
Ian	Russ
Jack	Ruth
Justin	Shula
Kirsty	Tom
Lilian	Tony
Lily	Usha

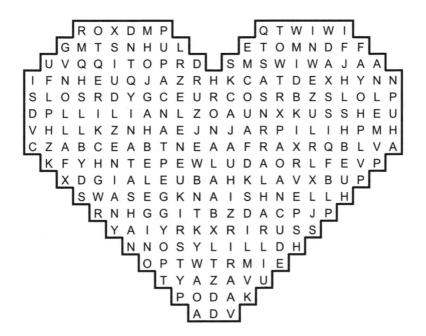

ANAGRAMS

Unscramble these anagrams to discover some properties in Ambridge.

1. HARM LEGAL BID

2. WE SHOUTED 'HERO!'

3. WE GOT LOCAL WIT

4. STEEL BATHS

5. VIA THE GRACE

MYSTERY SUDOKU

Complete the grid so that every row, column and 3 × 3 box contains the letters EGILNORST in any order. One row or column contains a character's surname of eight letters. What is it?

					R		S	
N		T			S	E		G
			G	N			R	T
		E				N	G	
	N	G				S		
O	E			S	G			
G		R	T			L		E
	I		N					

TAKE YOUR PICK

Which of the following is the correct answer? Take your pick.

1. There was great excitement when Shula and Kenton were born, but how did Jill and Phil decide on names for their twins?
   a) They picked names at random from the Borchester telephone directory.
   b) By throwing children's building blocks into the air. These blocks had letters on the sides and the names were formed this way.
   c) Shula Kenton was the author of a much-trusted recipe book that Jill owned. As it contained some of Phil's favourite dishes, they named the twins after the author.

2. Jill Archer received a police caution for throwing an item of food at a restaurateur during a protest about food waste. What did she throw?
   a) A currant bun
   b) A wholemeal bread roll
   c) A flapjack

3. How did Jack Woolley's dog Captain disgrace himself at Neil and Susan's wedding?
   a) He chased a cat into the hall as the wedding speeches were being made.
   b) Captain jumped up at Susan for a pat and muddied her dress.
   c) He ate the wedding cake.

WORD LADDER

Many in Ambridge enjoy meeting up at The Bull and, in this word ladder, you can do just that. Changing one letter at a time, go from 'meet' to 'Bull'.

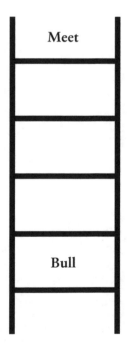

Meet

Bull

CRISS-CROSS

Many much-loved animals have regularly featured in *The Archers*. In this criss-cross, find homes for all the following in the grid.

4-letter names
Bess
Biff
Duff
Judy
Nell
Tara
Tess

5-letter names
Boxer
Comet
Fleur
Holly
Honey
Minty
Tolly

6-letter names
Eccles
Hermes

Magnet
Nimrod
Scruff
Silver
Turpin

7-letter names
Bettina
Demeter
Maxwell
Salieri
Tootsie
Trigger

8-letter names
Bartleby
Chandler
Midnight

10-letter name
Barbarella

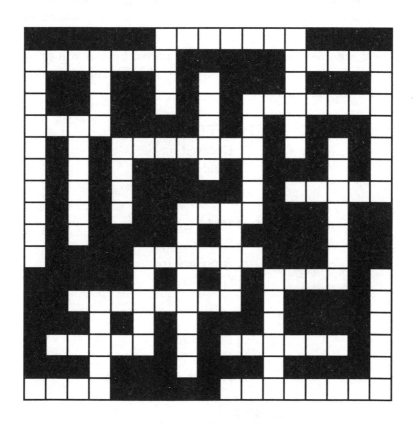

COUNTRY WORDS

There are many wonderful country words, but do you know the correct meaning of the following? They all come from the Midlands, aka Borsetshire.

1. DOATED
   a) Decayed timber
   b) Field left fallow
   c) Storm-damaged crops

2. RUNNEL
   a) Rabbit warren
   b) A pollard tree
   c) Small stream

3. COLLY
   a) Blackbird
   b) Fallow field
   c) Leather strap or harness

4. RIP
   a) Tarpaulin or cover
   b) Sheaf of corn
   c) Hen coop

HIDDEN DELIGHT

Place a three-letter word in the spaces in each row to complete a seven-letter word. When completed correctly, a new word in the shaded letters will be formed that is something that is much appreciated in Ambridge. What is the hidden delight?

P	L				B	O
N	E				S	T
P	A				N	T
R	E				E	D
W	E				N	D
I	L				A	L
A	M				U	R

NAME JIG

The names of five characters have been cut up into sections. Join the pieces together to see who they are.

AL

LY

TUC

CAR

TER

GOR

RG

AR

ET

NKS

LE

ER

LI

TRE

PA

AN

NDA

NE

CH

BRE

OL

JO

FRA

RAN

KER

CRYPTOGRAM

Solve the cryptogram to discover an interesting – and true – observation from Jennifer. To give you a start, Z = U, W = L and I = V.

ONE THING ABOUT THE

ARCHER FAMILY, THINGS

NEVER STOP HAPPENING,

DO THEY?

CROSSWORD

Across

1 Outer area of a city (6)
4 Lady of few words but was a cook and cleaner extraordinaire (5, 3)
9 Busy (6)
10 Ambridge family (8)
12 Not compulsory (8)
13 Hurt the feelings of (6)
15 The village's 'charming guesthouse!' (8, 4)
18 Tiger in exile? (4, 8)
23 She tried to tame 18A (6)
24 Lightweight metal (8)
26 Often at odds with brother (2, 6)
27 New hit (anag) (6)
28 Earnest request (8)
29 Spring flower (6)

Down

1 According to time of year (8)
2 Containers for washing (8)
3 Pasta dish (7)
5 Actor's part (4)
6 Grim (7)
7 Animal feed (6)
8 Produces (6)
11 Objectives (7)
14 Aromatic herb (7)
16 Of mind, body and spirit (8)
17 Bits and bobs (8)
19 Most of the time (2, 1, 4)
20 Climate (7)
21 Sheep's wool (6)
22 Tail of a dart (6)
25 Prepare for publication (4)

LETTER DROP

The letters in each of the columns need to be entered into the squares immediately below, but not necessarily in the same order. By placing the letters in the correct places, you will reveal something Helen wrote in the Autumn 2000 edition of the *Borchester Echo*.

MINI SUDOKU: QUINOA

As a vegan, Kate is likely to know a good few recipes with quinoa, though whether she can persuade Brian to try them remains to be seen. Complete the grid so that every row, column and 2 × 3 box contains the letters that make up 'quinoa'.

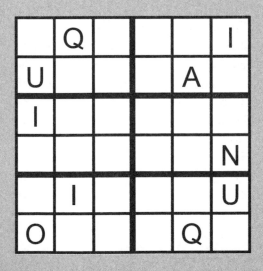

WORD SEARCH: DOGS

Round up the following dogs by finding them in the grid.

Bess	Leo
Bettina	Meg
Biff	Mitch
Captain	Nell
Charlie	Patch
Felicity	Portia
Georgina	Scruff
Gyp	Tag
Hermes	Tara
Holly	Tess
Honey	Trigger
Jet	Turpin
Judy	Winston

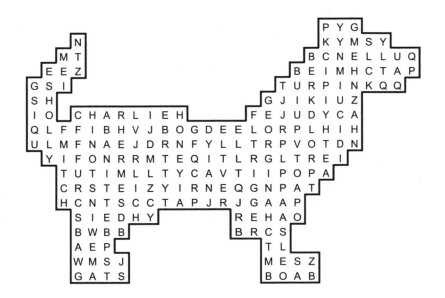

ANAGRAMS

Unscramble the following to reveal the names of some well-known characters.

1. THE LUCKY YEAR

2. IN LITTLE JOUST

3. A RASH HEART CAN!

4. RATHER CHIC REPORTS

5. MAINLY ALE BILL

NAME BUILDER

The letters of a nine-letter name have been numbered 1 to 9. Solve the clues to discover who it is.

Letters 2, 1, 4 and 5 give us an irritation

Letters 5, 8, 2 and 9 give us the next in line

Letters 4, 8, 7, 3, 9 and 6 give us a midpoint

Letters 6, 2, 1, 5, 8 and 9 give us one or the other

Letters 8, 7, 3, 2, 4 and 6 is to lure, something this character did with disastrous consequences.

1	2	3	4	5	6	7	8	9

ON TRACK

Starting with the circled letter and moving one letter at a time, either horizontally or vertically, find the first names of nine well-known characters.

(H)	E	A	N	C	I	E
E	L	I	R	L	R	O
N	A	N	B	A	R	L
L	I	Y	L	T	V	I
I	L	N	E	R	E	R
I	L	D	B	N	A	S
E	N	A	O	R	S	U

MYSTERY SUDOKU

Complete the grid so that every row, column and 3 × 3 box contains the letters CDEHMOPRU in any order. One row or column contains a seven-letter word, which is something of considerable value to farmers. What is it?

					E		H	O
	R		C		D		P	
D								R
E		P			U	C		
		O	H			R		U
R								C
	M		D		H		R	
O	H		U					

TRIVIA: PAST AND PRESENT

It's all go in Ambridge! Can you answer these wide-ranging posers?

1. Who cut through a telephone wire when pruning a clematis early in 2019?
2. In the 2006 production of *Snow White and the Seven (Slightly Taller Than Average) Dwarves*, who played Snow White?
3. A 'Three Peaks Challenge' was held in 2003. Lakey Hill and the church tower were two of the peaks. What was the third?
4. One of Freddie's fellow students supplied him with drugs to deal with. What was his first name?
5. What breed of cow did Helen import from France early in 2019?
6. In the Great Ambridge Bread Bake Off held in 2012, who was disqualified for using a bread maker?
7. Jill Archer announced that on her visits to see Chris at The Laurels, she had met a man. What is his name?
8. What was the cause of Nic Grundy's tragic death at the age of 37?
9. What unlikely job did PC Burns do while at university?
10. Who returned to Ambridge in 2018, a decade after first arriving in the village?

CRYPTOGRAM

Solve the cryptogram to discover a country saying. To give you a start, X = L and D = P.

I	T	K	F	K	'Z		J	E	I	T	G	J	P		M	E	F	Z	K
					'														

I	T	V	J		Z	X	V	A	N		D	V	J	I	Z,
						L					P				,

X	E	E	Z	K		W	E	E	I	Z		V	J	C		V
L																

A	V	D		I	T	V	I		C	E	K	Z	J	'I		H	G	I
		P												'				

CRISS-CROSS

All these familiar names have had a part in Ambridge life and they also form a part of the grid. Fit them into the right places.

3-letter names
Jim
Rex
Roy
Tom

4-letter names
Adam
Alan
Emma
Jill
Josh
Kate
Mike
Neil
Ruth
Tony
Usha
Will

5-letter names
Brian

David
Henry
Kathy
Lewis
Shula
Susan

6-letter names
Hayley
Jazzer
Jolene
Justin
Kenton
Kirsty
Robert
Ruairi

8-letter names
Alistair
Jennifer

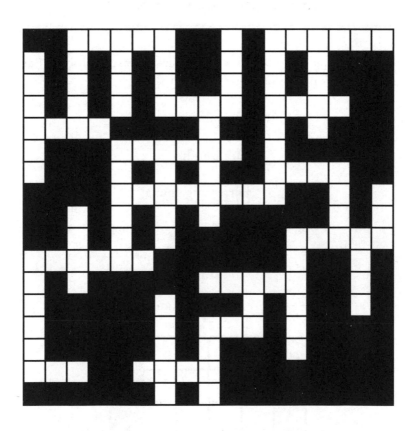

ACROSTICS

Solve the clues correctly and the shaded squares will reveal an extensive property in Ambridge. What is it?

1. An Ambridge farm

2. Surplus

3. Burrowing animal

4. Fibre used in basket-making

5. Thing

6. Move unsteadily

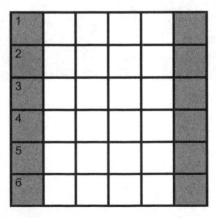

HIDDEN NAMES

A name is hidden in each of the following sentences. Can you find them?

1. In the next scene, I'll be able to show my acting prowess.

2. As there's not much time, we'll need to bypass the queue somehow.

3. It's Mum's sponge cake I rather like, especially if it has lots of jam.

4. If someone sends us another order, we will beat last month's sales figures.

CODED CROSSWORD

Each letter of the alphabet has been replaced by a number. To solve the puzzle, you must decide which letter is represented by which number. To help you start, one of the words has been partly filled in. When you have solved the code, complete the bottom grid to discover an organisation with interests in Ambridge. What is it?

8		6		12		16		24		2		18		10
5	1	5	24	11	14	11		11	4	19	2	10	21	14
12		15		11		15		22		13		26		10
10	13	24	11	15	2	20		17	19	4	20	25	26	2
2		19				17		11		25		6		5
5	26	4	17	3	5	26	4	17		11	23	11	26	2
				26				11		2		13		19
21	25	1	26	19	21	11		24	26	10	8	2	11	26
11		6		22		15				11				
9	25	11	11	13		20	5	6	8	24	19	16 Z	11 E	13 N
25		5		11		11		11				11		19
11	5	26	6	24	19	14		5	24	12	25	13	1	2
13		10		19		11		24		11		10		10
1	19	13	10	8	11	26		11	26	26	5	2	10	1
11		4		8		5		26		7		20		11

1	2	3	4	5	6	7	8	9	10	11 E	12	13 N
14	15	16 Z	17	18	19	20	21	22	23	24	25	26

24	5	14	5	26	5		1	5	15	10	2	5	6

WORD LADDER

The Hunt Ball is a much anticipated and enjoyed event on the Ambridge calendar. In this word ladder, changing one letter at a time, turn 'hunt' into 'ball'.

Hunt

Ball

LETTER DROP

The letters in each of the columns need to be entered into the squares immediately below, but not necessarily in the same order. By placing the letters in the correct places you will reveal a much-heard lament. What is it?

	R	D		I	A		
H	I	T		D	I		
Y	O	S		D	Y	M	E
W	G	E	U	N	T	E	V
T	H	A	U	D	H	O	N	E

(Grid with letters to be dropped into the squares below, including a `!` and a `?`)

COUNTRY WORDS

The Midlands, aka Borsetshire, is an area rich in fine country words. Do you know the correct meaning of the following?

1. CAN-BOTTLE
    a) The long-tailed tit
    b) Wasp
    c) Tankard

2. RINNICK
    a) Cattle food
    b) To plough lightly
    c) The smallest pig of a litter

3. FADY
    a) Field boundary
    b) Damp, humid weather
    c) Water trough

4. EEKLE
    a) The green woodpecker
    b) Earthworm
    c) Drizzle

THE MYSTERIOUS X

Solve the clues and a character's name will be formed in the X-shaped shaded squares.

1. Sincere, truthful

2. Celebrated

3. Human soul or mind

4. Leg joints

5. Hidden

6. Cure

TRUE OR FALSE?

Decide whether the following statements are true or false. They all relate to The Bull.

1. Barry, who hails from Penny Hassett, takes particular delight in bursting crisp packets.
2. The Bull was runner-up in the 2017 Best Pub Garden in Borsetshire competition.
3. At his ninety-second birthday party, Walter Gabriel was declared a freeman of The Bull.
4. The Bull features in a guide called *Best Pub Walks in Borsetshire*. On publication in 2017 it resulted in a great many ramblers calling in for a pint.
5. Former publican Sid Perks was a dab hand at a Yard of Ale competition and won quite a few contests over the years.
6. Jimmy Grange's skiffle group used to play at The Bull.
7. Marjorie Antrobus used to play shove ha'penny in a corner of The Bull.
8. Early in 2019 Kenton bought some vinyl records and decks for The Bull.
9. In 1995 Kathy Perks gave The Bull's restaurant a Civil War theme.
10. When The Bull's pub sign showed signs of weathering, Kenton set about touching the sign up himself.

WORD BUILDER

The letters of a nine-letter word have been numbered 1 to 9. Solve the clues to discover something seen and sought in Ambridge.

Letters 7, 3, 6 and 8 give us something tidy

Letters 5, 8, 3 and 1 give us a rung

Letters 1, 4, 7 and 9 give us some cookware

Letters 2, 4, 5, 8 and 3 involve hurry

Letters 5, 2, 6, 1 and 3 give us a form

1	2	3	4	5	6	7	8	9

ANAGRAMS

Unscramble the following to reveal some well-known names.

1. 'DERIDE' I GABBLED

2. BACKED RETURN

3. RASH UK FANS

4. REAP CHART

5. TRACE A RELIC

WORD QUEST: OLIVER

With his wide interests, willingness to support others – including the Grundys – and his involvement in Ambridge life, Oliver Sterling has, over the years, contributed a great deal to the village. He is very much part of the huntin', fishin' and shootin' brigade. In this word quest, make as many words as possible of three or more letters out of the name.

OLIVER

25 words = excellent
20 words = very good
15 words = good
10 words = fair effort
5 words = better luck next time!

CRYPTOGRAM

Solve the cryptogram to discover a seasonal observation from Tom Forrest. To give you a start, P = F and Z = P.

V	P		S	K	B		N	T	G		Z	R	T	G	D		S	K	B	W
	F										P									

P	K	K	D		B	Z	K	G		G	V	G	U		L	T	V	Y	V	U	Y
F						P															

D	A	U	G		Y	Z	W	V	G	F		A	T	Y		N	K	H	U
						P													

CRISS-CROSS: THE COUNTRYSIDE

Fit all the following sights of the countryside into the grid. A truly rural mix.

3-letter words
Ewe
Hay
Hog
Pig
Sty

4-letter words
Barn
Bull
Calf
Crop
Farm
Goat
Herd
Lamb
Mare

5-letter words
Hedge

Horse
Sheep
Straw
Wheat

6-letter words
Barley
Donkey
Heifer
Meadow
Plough
Stable

7-letter words
Combine
Paddock
Tractor

8-letter word
Cockerel

A PERPLEXING POSER

Lakey Hill is a much-admired landmark as well as a great place to enjoy scenic views of Ambridge and the Borsetshire countryside. Lakey Hill is also where many a courting couple have ventured, most notably when Mark Hebden proposed to Shula Archer at the top. It is also the site of some round barrows dating back to the Bronze Age. However, what is it…

that goes up Lakey Hill,
down Lakey Hill
and yet never moves?

MYSTERY SUDOKU

Complete the grid so that every row, column and 3 × 3 box contains the letters ABDEILRWY in any order. One row or column contains a nine-letter word that is often seen and appreciated in the countryside. What is it?

			L			D		I
D			R			Y		
Y		L	A					W
						I	W	
			I	R	L			
	L	A						
B					E	W		Y
		Y			R			E
L		W			Y			

CODED CROSSWORD

Each letter of the alphabet has been replaced by a number. To solve the puzzle, you must decide which letter is represented by which number. To help you start, one of the words has been partly filled in. When you have solved the code, complete the bottom grid to discover a popular tradition in Ambridge.

26	6	14	13	4	16		19	9	14	3	15	2
9		9		18		4		17		6		13
11	18	15	16		4	18	24	13	14	23	9	14	1	6
7		15		24		15		18		19		19
6	24	24	6	4	13		14	13	24	13	9	16	13	20
9				23		15		16		17		23
9	4	22	8	24	16	6	16	13		12	13	4	16
		9				18				9		
26	9	14	8		2	9	15	19	17	14	18	4	5
13		11		16		19		6				23
17	13	11	18	13	9	16	5		10	13	9	19	6	16
19		13		21		6		13		17		18
25	13	9	16(T)	5(H)	13(E)	14	8	9	2		17	9	14	2
14		14		14		13		1		6		13
4	9	22	15	2	1		12	13	4	16	13	20

1	2	3	4	5 H	6	7	8	9	10	11	12	13 E
14	15	16 T	17	18	19	20	21	22	23	24	25	26

| | | | | | ■ | | | ■ | | | | | |
| 4 | 16 | 15 | 14 | | | 18 | 24 | | 4 | 18 | 2 | 20 | 9 | 22 |

NAME JIG

The names of five characters have been cut up into sections. Join the pieces together to see who they are.

RRIE

TON

SUS

CY

AD

KER

KE

ARC

HER

AM

MI

CAR

CLA

KEN

GRU

MA

NDY

TER

AN

TUC

WORD BUILDER

The letters of something that has been much discussed in Ambridge have been numbered 1 to 9. Solve the clues to discover what it is.

Letters 8, 7 and 1 give us an enterprising young Archer

Letters 8, 9, 3 and 4 give us chatter

Letters 3, 7, 9 and 1 give us rich soil

Letters 5, 6, 2, 3 and 8 give us a counterpane

Letters 7, 9 and 4 give us a tree

Letters 5, 6, 2 and 8 cause us to give up,
but hopefully not this puzzle.

1	2	3	4	5	6	7	8	9

CRYPTOGRAM

Vanessa Whitburn was Editor of *The Archers* for 22 years and this cryptogram gives you the chance to discover an interesting behind-the-scenes observation. What did she say? To give you a start, I = M and G = W.

J	A	I	D		A	C		W	F	D		Q	V	O	O	D	J	W
	M																	

K	B	O	Z	I	D	Y	W	J		Q	D	W	G	D	D	Y
				M									W			

A	Z	B		G	B	V	W	D	B	J		K	B	D		A	P	D	B
				W															

W	F	D		E	F	K	B	K	E	W	D	B	J

MINI SUDOKU: TURKEY

The Grundys have a long tradition of rearing, plucking and selling turkeys. In this mini sudoku, complete the grid so that every row, column and 2 × 3 box contains the letters that make up the word 'turkey'.

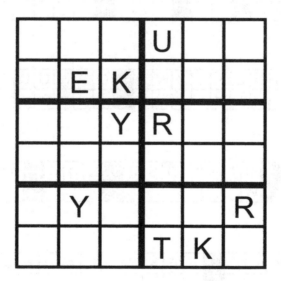

CROSS OUT

Cross out all the letters that appear more than once. The letters that are left, reading from top to bottom and left to right, will spell out an issue that has been a cause of contention in Ambridge.

H	B	N	E	G	L	A	F
T	Q	I	L	X	U	J	W
D	M	V	Y	Z	B	C	N
L	W	F	R	D	H	Z	L
U	O	D	W	V	B	T	P
J	Y	E	X	A	S	Q	I

FITTING WORDS

Enter the words below horizontally in the grid. These are all words likely to be heard in Ambridge. When the grid is completed, a word in the shaded boxes will be formed that is something used regularly in the village farms. What is it?

Blossom

Tearoom

Parlour

Cricket

Rearing

Country

Archers

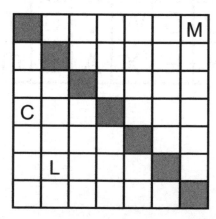

TRIVIA: PAST AND PRESENT

How clued up are you about Ambridge life? Test your knowledge with these tricky questions.

1. In 2007 Eddie Grundy bet someone that they could not give up alcohol for Lent. Who was this bet with?
2. When Nigel tragically fell to his death, who was on the Lower Loxley roof with him?
3. The Grundys' cider club is popular with some Ambridge residents. What did Eddie and Joe persuade Justin Elliott to provide for it?
4. Which of Rosie's middle names caused surprise and consternation with Jill?
5. What was Elizabeth's mistaken thought about the connection between Lily and Meredith?
6. What small business has Josh Archer set up?
7. Who built a shepherd hut for Lynda?
8. Who bought their own engagement ring?
9. There have been many weddings in Ambridge, but two weddings did not go ahead as planned on the day.
   a) Who jilted their bride at the altar?
   b) Which couple decided they did not need a piece of paper to prove their love and are now in a 'forever relationship'?

COUNTRY WORDS

The countryside is famed for its rich, colourful words but do you know the correct meaning of the following, all of which come from the Midlands, aka Borsetshire?

1. HILT
   a) Nail used in horse-shoeing
   b) Leather pouch
   c) A young sow

2. GAUN
   a) A wooden pail used in milking or brewing
   b) Horse blinkers
   c) Pole used by the thatcher to make a repair

3. MOUNDING
   a) A disease of sheep
   b) Fencing
   c) An outcrop of flint stones

4. SPITTER
   a) A weeding tool
   b) The nightjar
   c) Charcoal burner's furnace

FOLLOW THE LEADER

The names of three well-known characters have been entered below. The letters of the names are in the order in which they appear reading anti-clockwise. Starting from the R, bottom right, discover who they are.

T	R	H	Y	G	T	A
Y						O
P		R	Y	E		D
U		S		K		K
U				K		E
E	N	C	R	D		R

WEDDING BELLS

Put the following weddings in the order they occurred, from the earliest to the most recent.

a) Jennifer Travers-Macy and Brian Aldridge

b) Julia Pargetter and Lewis Carmichael

c) Pat Lewis and Tony Archer

d) Fallon Rogers and Harrison Burns

e) Peggy Archer and Jack Woolley

f) Usha Gupta and Alan Franks

g) Alice Aldridge and Christopher Carter

h) Doris Forrest and Dan Archer

i) Jolene Perks and Kenton Archer

j) Ruth Pritchard and David Archer

STRANGE BUT TRUE

Lynda has always taken great care with her appearance and was very excited when she heard about the facial product Lipoflora, but why did it cause her problems?

a) It caused her skin to come out in blotches, something she tried (unsuccessfully) to conceal because of the forthcoming church fete. At the fete, people kept commenting about her skin, making matters worse.

b) Lynda accidently spilled it, and the stain it left on her carpet was very difficult to remove. She took the manufacturers to task and they offered her some more – which she declined in no uncertain terms.

c) Despite the product having many recommendations, Lynda had great problems tracking it down.

WORD SEARCH: VEGETABLES

So much produce is grown and sold in Ambridge. Have fun digging out the following.

Artichoke

Beetroot

Broccoli

Cabbage

Carrot

Cauliflower

Celery

Chard

Cucumber

Kale

Kohlrabi

Leek

Marrow

Onion

Parsnip

Potato

Radish

Spinach

Swede

Turnip

```
P I N R U T N Z E M L K A I C
E C C H D O Y O U D T K L J H
K U T X I V X F T P E S E S W
O C O N C N O H A A N W I E N
H U O O A P I R J K T D S X L
C M R A U A S Q D S A O P T I
I B T L L N X T L R N K P L S
T E E V I E G A B B A C O P K
R R E P F Y I R C V C C I V A
A C B A L J S A Z H C N P G L
H K E V O P L X X O A T G Y E
F X I L W N C T R C Y R P Z A
F H W Q E C W B H Q D C D G P
Z W M M R R O K H M A R R O W
T O R R A C Y I B A R L H O K
```

TAKE YOUR PICK

Which of the following is the correct answer? Take your pick.

1. Phil Archer prided himself on the runner beans he produced every year for the Flower and Produce Show. What was the secret he once confided to Bert?
   a) He played music to them – always Radio 3
   b) He used liberal amounts of Brookfield dung
   c) He soaked the seeds in diluted ale for 24 hours before planting

2. What did Greg Turner train his dog Mitch to do?
   a) Growl whenever he heard the name Matt Crawford
   b) Stand on his hind legs on command, and walk round in a large circle, always finishing off where he started
   c) Find and retrieve golf balls

3. At his wedding to Elizabeth, Nigel Pargetter opted for a more environmentally friendly alternative to paper confetti. What was it?
   a) Rice
   b) Dried flower petals
   c) Bird seed

4. Pat Archer was once the county champion in what sport?
   a) Trampolining
   b) Javelin
   c) Discus

WORD LADDER

Home Farm is the centre of so much activity and industry – in this word ladder, change one letter at a time to transform 'Home' into 'Farm'.

Home

Farm

BETWEEN THE LINES

Something that's enjoyed by many listeners of *The Archers* can be inserted in the blank line so that, reading downward, seven three-letter words are formed. What is the word hidden between the lines?

N	I	O	R	E	B	A
T	P	E	P	B	G	S

ANAGRAMS

Unscramble the following to reveal some well-known names.

1. REGRETTABLE PIT HAZE

2. BOLDLY NEED HAND

3. SURE CAN STAR

4. BIG ELDER BADDIE

5. I CRAVED HARD

MYSTERY SUDOKU

Complete the grid so that every row, column and 3 × 3 box contains the letters ACELNRTUV in any order. One row or column contains a seven-letter word that at one time caused great problems in Ambridge.

				L	E		E	
	C		R		A			
	V			T		N	R	
	R	U		N				
L								E
				U		A	N	
	N	A		C			L	
			V		T		C	
		C		R				

ON TRACK

Enjoy a stroll around Ambridge. Starting with the circled letter and moving one letter at a time, either horizontally or vertically, find four fine buildings.

B	R	I	R	K	W	R
U	R	D	A	M	G	I
H	C	G	A	R	H	T
C	H	E	F	L	A	H
S	N	E	H	L	T	H
S	T	E	P	B	A	E
T	S	S	E	L	T	S

A PERPLEXING POSER

Archers, they have one.
Pargetters have two,
but Grundys no, they don't have any.

What?

WHAT THEY SAID

The following are quotes from Walter Gabriel, Bert Fry and Jill Archer but with some of the words missing. What did they actually say?

1. Walter Gabriel often said,

> *'I know when I _____'*
> a) 'ave put me foot in it.
> b) ain't a-wanted.
> c) should've kept me trap shut.

2. After Bert Fry won a nettle eating competition, he said,

> *'According to Hippocrates, a mixture of nettles, pigeon dung and cumin is _____'*
> a) a good aphrodisiac.
> b) a very good "pick me up".
> c) very good for encouraging hair growth.

3. When Jill was considering the changes she had seen, she said,

> *'That's the trouble with farming these days. There _____'*
> a) are so many rules and regulations.
> b) are so few people to draw on at busy times.
> c) is not the money in it that there once was.

HIDDEN DELIGHTS

Each of the following words has a letter missing. When entered correctly, the missing letters will spell a particular delight of Ambridge. What is it? The answer is two words.

1. S H O _ E

2. W H _ L E

3. _ E R V E

4. B L _ S S

5. S T O _ Y

6. H _ T C H

7. T A _ E D

ANAGRAMS

Unscramble the following to reveal some well-known names.

1. DUMMY ANGER

2. RICH PAPER

3. BLANDLY HELD HOUSE

4. WHIMSICAL CEREAL

5. DARNED BIG LIAR

CROSS OUT

Cross out all the letters that appear more than once. The letters that remain, reading from top to bottom and left to right, will spell out an important role in Ambridge.

F	H	J	P	S	D	L	T
B	Q	U	G	R	X	I	V
Z	W	O	P	E	Y	J	X
U	L	V	C	R	W	K	L
R	M	I	Q	E	G	D	Y
D	F	H	A	B	U	N	Z

AN AMBRIDGE RIDDLE

My first is in pen but not in ink,
My second is in copper but not in zinc.
My third is in large as well as in small,
My fourth is in coat but not in shawl.
My fifth is caught but not in sort,
And should you do this
You could find yourself in Borchester court.

What is the word?

CRYPTOGRAM

Solve the cryptogram to discover something said by a certain character. Whose words are they? To give you a start, D = L and N = U.

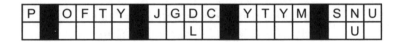

Row 1: P · O F T Y · J G D C · Y T Y M · S N U
(hint: L below D in JGDC; U below N in SNU)

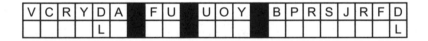

Row 2: V C R Y D A · F U · U O Y · B P R S J R F D
(hint: L below D in VCRYDA; L below D in BPRSJRFD)

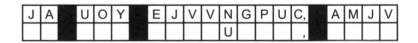

Row 3: J A · U O Y · E J V V N G P U C , · A M J V
(hint: U below N in EJVVNGPUC)

Row 4: V J U P T Y R · J A · S N M Y · F D U M N P R V
(hint: U below N in SNMY; L below D and U below N in FDUMNPRV)

MINI SUDOKU: YOGURT

Bridge Farm take great pride in their organic yogurt – this mini sudoku gives you a chance to reflect on this popular product. Complete the grid so that every row, column and 2 × 3 box contains the letters that make up the word 'yogurt'.

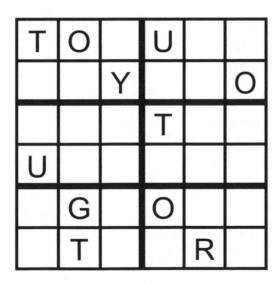

CRISS-CROSS: THE ARCHER FAMILY

Here's a chance to bring together some of the Archer family, past and present, by fitting them all into the grid.

3-letter names
Ben
Dan
Pat
Pip
Tom

4-letter names
Jack
Jill
John
Josh
Phil
Ruth
Tony

5-letter names
David
Doris
Frank
Grace
Helen
Henry
Laura

6-letter names
Jolene
Kenton
Meriel

COUNTRY WORDS

What are the correct meanings of these wonderful country words, which come from the Midlands, aka Borsetshire?

1. TALLET
    a) Hay loft over a stable
    b) Hand cart
    c) Horse's halter

2. SQUOYLE
    a) A weighted stick used by poachers
    b) Young stoat
    c) Bird scarer

3. SOUGHING
    a) Skimming the cream off milk
    b) Raking
    c) Digging drains

4. KIVE
    a) Dusk
    b) A large tub
    c) A piebald animal

WORD LADDER

The shop at Bridge Farm sells so much appetising produce. In the word ladder below, change one letter at a time to turn the word 'farm' into 'shop'.

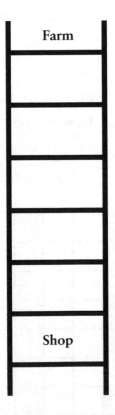

Farm

Shop

HIDDEN RESOURCE

Solve the clues correctly, and a place of considerable activity
– and also of much recent discussion in Ambridge – will be
revealed in the shaded squares. What is it?

1. Contagious disease

2. Perfect

3. Truck

4. Australian marsupial

5. Figure of speech

6. Link

7. Splendour

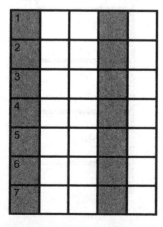

WHAT HAPPENED NEXT?

In the 2007 Flower and Produce Show a burst pipe caused a mass evacuation. This gave Derek Fletcher an opportunity to switch the labels on the runner beans in an attempt to deny victory to Bert Fry. But what happened next?

a) Although alone when switching the labels, his actions were observed through a window by Alan Franks. After a private admonishment, Derek Fletcher confessed to the judges what he had done. In view of his obvious regret, the matter was quietly dropped, and Bert Fry won the competition.

b) Seeing what had happened, Phil Archer switched the labels back, allowing Bert Fry to win.

c) In view of the chaos caused by the burst pipe, the show was abandoned and no prize was awarded.

d) Derek Fletcher won the prize, although a couple of days later one of his prized garden gnomes was smashed. Sweet revenge for Bert, although nothing was ever proved.

e) When it was discovered what Derek Fletcher had done, all his entries were disqualified. This meant that the prize he had won for the longest carrot now went to Phil, and the prize for the best lettuce went to Robert Snell, which delighted Lynda.

WORD BUILDER

The letters of a nine-letter word have been numbered 1 to 9. Solve the clues to discover something that is very important to the economy of Ambridge.

Letters 3, 2 and 6 give us a star

Letters 4, 2 and 9 give us a purchase

Letters 1, 5, 8 and 7 give us something difficult

Letters 4, 8, 5, 6, 7 and 9 give us an alcoholic spirit

Letters 5, 4, 3, 2, 8 and 7 give us something ridiculous

1	2	3	4	5	6	7	8	9

ANAGRAMS

Unscramble the following to reveal some well-known names.

1. HELD BEYOND LAND

2. ARRANGE NO RANT

3. DURING MAY

4. RARE PATCH

5. IN OUR VAIN ROAD

WORD QUEST: JUSTIN

Smooth-talking Justin Elliott has a great way with words, and here is a chance to consider words that can be made out of Justin's name. Make as many words of three or more letters out of 'Justin'. No plurals or abbreviations.

JUSTIN

12 words = excellent
9 words = very good
6 words = not bad
3 words = better luck next time!

149

DOWN WORD

Place a three-letter word in the spaces in each row to complete a six-letter word. When the grid is completed correctly, a new word in the shaded letters will be formed; this refers to some of the more unusual residents of Ambridge. What are they?

			A	C	A
			E	S	T
			M	E	R
			A	R	T
			D	I	T
			E	S	S

NAME JIG

The names of five characters have been cut up into sections. Join the pieces together to find who they are.

IAN TU NE ER BE

DD

TH

AR TER TTER RU

AMY CH ROY CAR

CKER PA

LL

RGE FRE IE LIL

IL

LETTER DROP

The letters in each of the columns need to be entered into the squares immediately below, but not necessarily in the same order. By putting the letters in the correct places you will reveal Brian Aldridge's way of thinking.

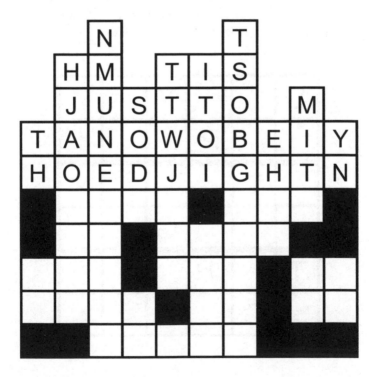

MINI SUDOKU: PIGSTY

The topic of pig farming in Ambridge has provoked much discussion, especially on the merits of large-scale indoor pig farming compared to pigs being raised outdoors. In this mini sudoku, complete the grid so that every row, column and 2 × 3 box contains the letters that make up the word 'pigsty'.

S			Y		
		P			I
	T				Y
			G		
T		I			
	G				

TRIVIA: NAMES

1. What is the name of Rob Titchener's mother?

2. What did Rob Titchener want to call the baby boy he had with Helen?

3. When Eddie Grundy entered the B&B business, he was troubled by the awkward demands and questions of a potential guest, Harriet Vane. But who actually was Harriet Vane?

4. Who was known as 'the Lily of Layton Cross'?

5. Alice was tempted by a job in which Canadian city?

6. What was the name of Justin Elliott's wife?

7. What sort of animal is Hilda Ogden? Who owns her, and who owned her before?

8. Bruno Milna wrote over one thousand scripts for *The Archers* but he was better known as someone else. What was Bruno Milna's real name?

9. Who was 'the dog woman?'

10. What is Peppa Pig?

CRISS-CROSS: AMBRIDGE RESIDENTS

Ambridge certainly has had a rich and diverse mix of characters. In this criss-cross, enjoy adding all the following well-known names to the grid.

3-letter names
Jim
Rex
Roy

4-letter names
Adam
Alan
Emma
Jill
Josh
Kate
Mike
Neil

Tony
Usha
Will

5-letter names
Brian
David
Helen
Henry

6-letter names
Hayley
Jazzer
Jolene

Justin
Kenton
Kirsty
Oliver
Robert
Ruairi

7-letter name
Clarrie

8-letter names
Alistair
Jennifer

CRYPTOGRAM

According to the *Borchester Echo*, this was overheard in Underwoods department store. Solve the cryptogram to find what was said. To give you a start, Q = U and S = F.

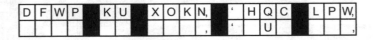

D	F	W	P		K	U		X	O	K	N,		'	H	Q	C		L	P	W,
											,			'	U					,

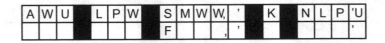

A	W	U		L	P	W		S	M	W	W,	'		K		N	L	P	'U
								F			,	'							'

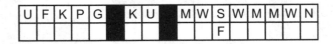

U	F	K	P	G		K	U		M	W	S	W	M	M	W	N
											F					

U	L		X	F	L	W	X

WHAT COULD POSSIBLY GO WRONG?

1. In 2004 the W.I. held a Simnel cake competition. To her dismay, Lynda Snell's entry was disqualified. Why?
    a) The cake had a soggy bottom.
    b) Lynda had frozen the cake and it had not fully defrosted in time.
    c) The crust was so hard that Ian, the judge, could not cut into it.

2. What happened to Walter Gabriel's marrow at the 1982 Flower and Produce Show?
    a) It exploded.
    b) On inspection, part of the marrow was rotten and it was discovered that Walter had used skin from another marrow to conceal the rotten part. As a consequence, all of Walter's entries that year were disqualified.
    c) It was so heavy it broke the table on which it was displayed and destroyed several other exhibits as well. It was decided not to award a prize for the biggest marrow that year, something that annoyed Walter as he considered his was the biggest marrow, 'the likes of which Ambridge had never seen'.

WORD LADDER

The relationship between Lily and Russ has had its fair share of problems and raised a few eyebrows. In this word ladder, changing one letter at a time, turn the name 'Lily' to 'Russ'.

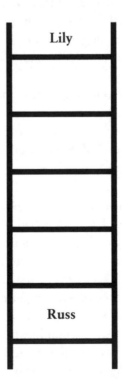

Lily

Russ

HIDDEN NAMES

A name is concealed in each of the following sentences. Can you find who is hiding away?

1. Although some of my plans have involved quite an upheaval, I certainly think everything has worked out for the best.

2. He was unusually annoyed and outspoken tonight, but quickly calmed down.

3. I like to follow a system, mainly because that way I know I can get more done.

4. I think it is important to be enthusiastic. A role model for others can work wonders.

WORD SEARCH: WEATHER

In a farming community, so much is dependent on the weather. In this word search, can you find all these weather conditions?

bright	misty
cloudy	overcast
damp	rainy
dry	snowy
dull	stormy
foggy	sunny
frosty	thunder
hot	warm
lightning	windy
mild	

```
M K S M P H I F B R O V B G D
F L I H T W P H Y D U O L C M
I L V G H A Z M B B Y I Y O F
D T C N U Y G G A G G F Q O Y
W S T I N I T F S D X A G Z A
P A A N D Y T S T G P G O C A
L C M T E Y R D O G Y K I A D
F R H H R A P U R R W N L J B
C E X G V B G S M Y F M R A W
K V T I Y T M U Y U W Z R V S
A O H L Y N J I F U F O G N S
U Q G K R U I D S L D V N F U
F O I L G J H A G T T U W S N
A X R G X M Q W R N Y O L E N
T X B F Q G Y W I N D Y H L Y
```

STRANGE BUT TRUE

In 1983 mystery was afoot when the Over-60s' club tea money went missing. The local bobby was called in to investigate. What had happened?

a) Jethro Larkin had borrowed the money to tide him over for the next few days. He had every intention of repaying the money and had even put an IOU note in a ledger to that effect. He made good his promise and added a bit more.
b) Mrs Perkins, or Mrs P as she was known, had found coins on the floor and put them in a charity tin. It was only a few days later that she heard about the missing tea money and, by then, the investigation had started. The theory was that the caddy containing the money had been knocked over without anyone being aware.
c) Clive Horrobin came under great suspicion as he was seen in the area, but nothing was ever proved.
d) The money was found in the caddy but more loose tea leaves had been poured over it and then the wrong lid had been placed on top of the caddy.

WORD BUILDER

The letters of a nine-letter word have been numbered 1 to 9. Solve the clues to discover something that performs a useful function in Ambridge fields.

Letters 2, 7, 5 and 9 give us a ship's company

Letters 7, 3, 4 and 5 give us something uncommon

Letters 1, 6, 8, 4 and 5 give us twenty

Letters 9, 8, 5 and 1 give us misfortunes

Letters 1, 8, 6, 2, 5 and 4 give us a ball game

1	2	3	4	5	6	7	8	9

MYSTERY SUDOKU

Complete the grid so that every row, column and 3 × 3 box contains the letters ABDEGMORS in any order. One row or column contains a seven-letter word that is the subject of some controversy in Ambridge. What is it?

	S							A
				E	R			M
G		M			S			B
				R	O		S	
	D						B	
	O		B	D				
R			S			E		O
D			A	M				
E							A	

TAKE YOUR PICK

Which of the following is the correct answer? Take your pick.

1. Why was Lynda Snell annoyed with Larry Lovell's review of her 1999 production *Babes in the Millennium Wood*?
    a) He spelled 'Lynda' with an 'i', which infuriated her.
    b) He focused on the smell of pig manure rather than the merits of the production.
    c) He kept referring to the wobbling scenery.

2. The Cellar Club opened in Ambridge in 1963 in which building?
    a) The Bull
    b) The village hall
    c) Arkwright Hall

3. What is the Borchester Beauty?
    a) A spring flower
    b) An apple
    c) A breed of pig

4. As an April Fool's joke Eddie told Joe that their cows needed to be photographed. What did he claim was the reason?
    a) The police were assembling a database of cow photos to prevent theft.
    b) There was a £1,000 prize in the *Borchester Echo* for the best-looking cow.
    c) A photo was needed for their soon-to-be-mandatory passports.

WORD SEARCH: WELL-KNOWN NAMES

Find all the following well-known names.

Brian	Kathy
David	Kirsty
Eddie	Mike
Emma	Neil
Fallon	Oliver
Hayley	Pip
Helen	Ruth
Henry	Shula
Jazzer	Susan
Jolene	Tom
Justin	Tony
Kate	Will

```
F O V K J L Y E U A E F N T Z
N A R U T H L U W N E L E H D
F Z L M W W G I Q S X S E A U
Y N A L J E S J W O Q T A A H
T A J K O A X E L W O H W K E
S I L H Z N T I G M P U T T A
R R L I E N V K Y Y H T A K J
I B B O J E H S C E T K P I P
K V G I R L Y L H F L B Y C W
J N H N A S U S Y U P Y Z K F
L O N I T S U J R A L K A Y E
E U L W R X U E N M P A R H I
P Z Y E N G I H E M D I V A D
M I K E N E L L H E T O N Y D
M J E F M E C R E Z Z A J U E
```

A PICTURE POSER

What is suggested by the following pictures? It's something that has become popular in Ambridge of late.

PIGS AND COWS

Pigs and cows are important to the economy of Ambridge. This puzzle involves the words 'pig' and 'cow'. The answers to clues 1–7 all start with the word 'pig', while the answers to clues 8–10 all start with the word 'cow'. The number of letters in the answer is given in parentheses after the clue. For example: this cow is a brightly patterned shell (5) would have the answer 'cowry'.

1. This pig flies (6)
2. This pig is a plait of hair (7)
3. This pig is a colour or dye (7)
4. This pig is stubborn (3-6)
5. This pig gives a ride (9)
6. This pig is good for savers (5, 4)
7. This pig sorts into compartments (10)
8. This cow is a spring flower (7)
9. This cow lacks courage (6)
10. This cow shrinks in fear (5)

ANAGRAMS

Unscramble the following to reveal some well-known names.

1. HIDE BOLDER PAGE

2. OVER TELLING, SIR?

3. I GAIN CAR

4. ARTICLE CARE

5. BURNED RACKET

CRYPTOGRAM

Solve the cryptogram to reveal a quote from a well-known character. Who said these words in a moment of exasperation? To give you a start, F = G and M = H.

Y	M	U	X		C	G	B	Z		U		F	K	O	T		M	U	R	B
	H											G					H			

X	G		C	G		X	G		F	B	X		U		C	O	K	S	J
									G										

O	G	A	S	C		M	B	O	B	?
						H				?

CRISS-CROSS: DOGS

Show some dogged determination as you find a home for all these Ambridge canines in this pooch-shaped grid.

3-letter names
Gyp
Jet
Leo
Meg
Tag

4-letter names
Bess
Biff
Judy
Nell
Tara
Tess

5-letter names
Butch
Holly
Honey

Mitch
Patch
Pippa
Timus

6-letter names
Hermes
Portia
Scruff

7-letter names
Bettina
Captain
Charlie

8-letter names
Felicity
Georgina

MINI SUDOKU: PLOUGH

The plough is an important piece of equipment on many a farm, and Ambridge has enjoyed some very competitive ploughing matches over the years. Bert Fry, in particular, prides himself on being able to plough 'a long straight furrow'. In this mini sudoku, complete the grid so that every row, column and 2 × 3 box contains the letters that make up the word 'plough'.

	G			O	
		H			
			P	G	
U					H
H		L	G		

A PERPLEXING POSER

Lynda Snell always likes to put on a grand show and make a great impression. In this puzzle, fill in the blanks using the *same* seven letters in the *same order* in each case.

After Lynda's _____ production, she was ___ ___ to serve canapés as she had ___ ___.

COUNTRY WORDS

Here are some more lovely country words from the Midlands, aka Borsetshire. What are their correct meanings?

1. CREE
   a) Nail used for horseshoes
   b) Pigsty
   c) Butter churn

2. DROCK
   a) Young hen
   b) A drain or ditch
   c) To trim or cut back a hedge

3. HOB
   a) A swarm of bees
   b) A clearing in the wood
   c) Awns of barley

4. JOBBET
   a) A horse's bit
   b) Bucket in a well
   c) Small load of hay

HIDDEN NAMES

A name has been smuggled in to each of the following sentences. Can you find who is hiding there?

1. The sample jars of fruit jam I expected from Ambridge Organics have just arrived.

2. I believe the decision of the board was just. I now need signatures in order for the scheme to go ahead.

3. I am hoping he lends his full support to the new breed.

4. After the promotion, the number of lamb enquiries doubled, much to my relief.

ACROSTICS

Solve the clues correctly and two words in the shaded squares will spell out something that is important to the Ambridge economy. What is it?

1. Drainage channel

2. Fruit

3. Central

4. Circular

5. Parts of eggs

1				
2				
3				
4				
5				

FOLLOW THE LEADER

The names of three well-known characters have been entered below. The letters of the names are in the order in which they appear, reading anti-clockwise. Starting from the I, bottom right, discover who they are.

R	I	M	C	V	N	A
L						I
A		E	D	H		A
D		R		Y		D
L				C		J
I	A	R	G	O		I

TAKE YOUR PICK

Which is the correct answer? Take your pick.

1. In one vivid scene Brian had an unpleasant encounter with a mad cow who kicked out at him. How did the sound effects team come up with a suitable sound?
   a) They hit a water melon with a hammer
   b) A studio technician gargled some mouthwash
   c) Someone on a pogo stick jumped up and down in a sand pit filled with mud.

2. What was found in 1995 on land belonging to Grange Farm?
   a) Celtic coins
   b) The remains of a German plane
   c) A hoard of banknotes that had been stolen a month before in a raid on a bank in Felpersham.

3. Tom Forrest enjoyed singing and he often sang about what feature in Ambridge?
   a) The bells of St Stephen's
   b) The village pump
   c) Lakey Hill

4. Rex Fairbrother used to be a professional in which sport?
   a) Football
   b) Wrestling
   c) Rugby

ANAGRAMS

Unscramble the following to reveal some fondly remembered characters.

1. DEAR RANCH

2. ENABLING ROLES

3. 'N' DRINK ALE

4. OR TEST FORM

5. KID PRESS

CRYPTOGRAM

Solve the cryptogram to reveal some words of wisdom from Walter Gabriel's granny. To give you a start, Y = C and M = P.

Y	H	L	Z		E	H		E	R	Z		M	H	D	C	E		X	C	A
C												P								

T	Z	E		E	R	Z	B	Z		P	N	D	Y	I,
													C	,

U	R	D	V	V	Q	-	U	R	X	V	V	Q	D	C	T		L	X	I	Z	U
						-															

L	Z		U	D	Y	I
					C	

WHO DID WHAT?

Match the person to their job.

1. Richard Locke   a) chef

2. Greg Turner   b) policeman

3. Jean-Paul   c) solicitor

4. Anisha Jayakody   d) vicar

5. Christopher Carter   e) secret agent

6. Dave Barry   f) vet

7. Titcombe   g) doctor

8. Mark Hebden   h) gamekeeper

9. Mike Daly   i) farrier

10. Robin Stokes   j) gardener

WORD SEARCH: PONIES AND HORSES

Round up the following ponies and horses.

Bartleby	Maxwell
Basil	Midnight
Blossom	Minty
Boxer	Nimrod
Chandler	Pluto
Comet	Silver
Duff	Spearmint
Fleur	Sylvester
Grey Silk	Tolly
Magnet	Tootsie
Maisie	

```
F B K K S I P S H L U R F P E
K A L C H G W T E N G A M R Y
C S L T O P L U T O L O V T S
P I E O B M O S S O L B N Y W
P L W O H S E I Q D V I L V D
B F X T T C T T O E M V P S M
A M A S Y O I R Z I E D U F F
R H M I N D M Z B S H R U J F
T X E E E I I L T I M E N C K
L C H A N D L E R A S V N B V
E R U E L F R U C M Q L I U R
B O N T D S P E A R M I N T W
Y Y L L O T F G R E Y S I L K
M I D N I G H T J B P F A Z Z
O Y Q N D P V L R E X O B U C
```

CRISS-CROSS: ISSUES

Over the years *The Archers* has covered – and raised awareness of – many issues. The following are just some of them. Find a place for them in the grid.

5 letters
Arson
Drugs

6 letters
Racism
Sepsis

7 letters
GM crops
Organic
Robbery
Suicide

8 letters
Abortion
Bovine TB

Eviction
Flooding
Gambling

9 letters
Hit and run
Surrogacy

10 letters
Bankruptcy
Depression

13 letters
Civil marriage
Community shop
Contamination
Domestic abuse

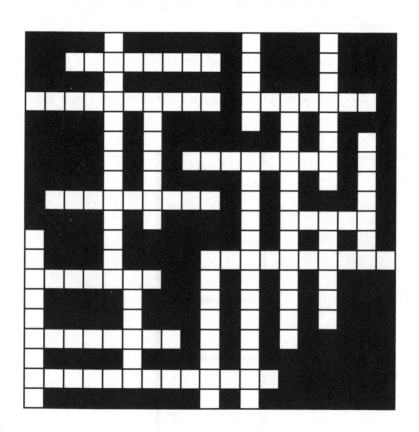

WORD LADDER

Ambridge farmers sow vast quantities of seed each year to ensure a good crop. In this word ladder there is a chance to help the process: by changing one letter at a time, turn 'seed' into 'crop'.

Seed

Crop

MINI SUDOKU: JUSTIN

With his wealth, influence and business interests, Justin Elliott is often at centre stage, and this puzzle is no different. In this mini sudoku, complete the grid so that every row, column and 2 × 3 box contains the letters that make up his name.

T					
	U		J		
	S				T
			U		N
J	I		T		

CODED CROSSWORD

Each letter of the alphabet has been replaced by a number. To solve the puzzle, you must work out which letter is represented by which number. To help you start, one of the words has been filled in. When you have solved the code, complete the grid at the bottom of the page to discover a popular event in the Ambridge calendar. In which month does this event take place?

NAME JIG

The names of five characters have been cut up into sections. Join the pieces together to see who they are.

BU

IAN

EM

DGE

WOO

DRI

GGY

GR

SNE

LL

RRI

HA

BR

RO

UN

PE

AL

MA

LLEY

BE

DY

RNS

RT

SON

WHAT THEY SAID

1. Walter Gabriel often quoted his granny. How did she end this particular saying?

    'No matter how humble, how rough or how rude
    A man should _____'
    a) be willing to show gratitude.
    b) have a pleasing attitude.
    c) never be lewd.

2. Dan Archer achieved success in growing carrots for the Flower and Produce Show by planting them in sand. However, Walter Gabriel commented that they tasted horrible, *'like _____'*

    a) sunburnt chipboard.
    b) a mouthful of grit.
    c) stale breadcrumbs.

3. How does one of Bert Fry's best-known sayings end?

    'Who doffs his coat on a winter's day _____'
    a) will soon lament his stupid way.
    b) will gladly put it on in May.
    c) will never keep the chill at bay.

MYSTERY SUDOKU

Complete the grid so that every row, column and 3 × 3 box contains the letters AELMPRSTU in any order. One row or column contains a seven-letter word that is an important commodity in Ambridge. What is it?

			E	P		U	L	
			T			M		
L		M	R				E	
						E		P
	R						A	
A		S						
	T				S	R		L
		U			R			
	E	A		L	T			

WORD SEARCH: UNSUNG CHARACTERS

The Archers has had a cast of many hundreds, with some characters appearing only briefly, some referred to but never heard, and others playing a small yet significant part. But no matter who they are, they have all contributed in some way to life in Ambridge. In this word search, pay tribute to some of the lesser-known but still important characters by finding the following:

Alan Carey	Jim Price
Albert Gibbs	Joe Blower
Ann Fraser	John Higgs
Baggy	Sam Peters
Betty Hood	Sid Jones
Bill Insley	Snatch Foster
Bill Morris	Sue Warren
Colin Drury	Titcombe
Fred Lamb	Trina Muir
Harold Bagley	
Haydn Evans	
Jess Allard	

```
N S A N D A B E Y E R A C N A L A
G C Y E A L B E R T G I B B S C A
D P E B C P T D R A L L A S S E J
O L L I T I T C O M B E A Z I J W
O D G L R W R C O L I N D R U R Y
H L A L I W M P S M N J S H M S F
Y S B I U T W R M F U N X H S J B
T G D N M P R Q R I A E A I P V M
T G L S A H H A X T J Y D S E R A
E I O L N A S Y C E D J A D F Y L
B H R E I E I H H N O M M Y G W D
T N A Y R U F Q E N P U W G W N E
K H H O T O N V E E M T A N D B R
I O V Y S H A S T S V B L F S J F
D J O T O N O E S U E W A R R E N
J G E R S I R R O M L L I B M L N
B R I B G S J O E B L O W E R G U
```

ANAGRAMS

Unscramble the following to reveal some fondly remembered characters.

1. HER RICH PAL

2. IS A TRUE-BORN MAJOR

3. REGRETTING PLEA

4. BORN ALL SEEING

5. GIRL'S INTOLERANCE

COUNTRY WORDS

Those in the countryside have their own rich language, but do you know the correct meaning of the following words, all of which come from the Midlands, aka Borsetshire?

1. DRAPE
a) Barren cow or sheep
b) A cart
c) Wooden cask

2. DACK
a) Deteriorating weather
b) Compost heap
c) To remove weeds

3. BOUT
a) Gate
b) Milking parlour
c) Rabbit hole

4. CUB
a) Hen coop
b) Trimmed hedgerow
c) Thatcher's hod

MINI SUDOKU: STABLE

One of the most dramatic moments in the long history of *The Archers* was when Grace Archer raced into a burning stable to try to rescue a horse. The horse survived but sadly Grace did not. The tragedy left husband Phil devastated and had a great impact on life in Ambridge. In this mini sudoku, complete the grid so that every row, column and 2 × 3 box contains the letters that make up the word 'stable'.

		T		S	
S			L	B	
A	S				
B		A			
				A	B

BETWEEN THE LINES

The name of someone fondly remembered can be inserted in the blank line so that, reading downward, eight three-letter words are formed. What is the name hidden between the lines?

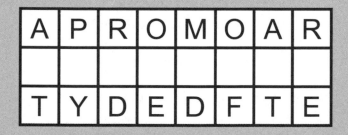

A	P	R	O	M	O	A	R
T	Y	D	E	D	F	T	E

WORD BUILDER

The letters of a nine-letter word have been numbered 1 to 9. Solve the clues to discover something seen in Ambridge.

Letters 5, 6 and 9 give us a gardening tool

Letters 1, 6, 2 and 4 give us froth

Letters 8, 7, 3 and 9 give us something that is certain

Letters 1, 9, 2 and 3 give us a feeling of dread

Letters 1, 2, 4, 6, 7 and 8 give us something celebrated, like *The Archers*

1	2	3	4	5	6	7	8	9

CRYPTOGRAM

Solve this cryptogram to find out how Dan once described Walter's voice. To give you a start, E = L and W = U.

E	Q	U	P			O		B	W	L	M	V			A	O	Q	E		Z	P	Q	A	K
L									U									L						

S	B	Q	I	P	A		M	X	B	R	W	K	X		M	X	P
											U						

Z	R	M	M	R	G		R	N		O		T	R	T	R	O		M	Q	A

CODED CROSSWORD

Each letter of the alphabet has been replaced by a number. To solve the puzzle, you must decide which letter is represented by which number. To help you start, one of the words has been partly filled in. When you have solved the code, complete the bottom grid to discover a name significant in the history of *The Archers*. What is the name and the significance?

MINI SUDOKU: LARKIN

The Larkins certainly added colour to Ambridge life, with Bob a bit of a rogue, Jethro a true yokel and Ned having a great sense of fun. On one occasion Ned had the misfortune to crash through some floorboards at Arkwright Hall, only to find some gold sovereigns! Clarrie too started life as a Larkin. In this mini sudoku, complete the grid so that every row, column and 2 × 3 box contains the letters that make up the name 'Larkin'.

			A		
N				K	
K					
		R	I		
R	L	I			

TAKE YOUR PICK

Which is the correct answer to these questions, which may bring back memories from long ago? Take your pick.

1. What did Jack Woolley do in 1990 that outraged Mrs Perkins and some others in the village?
   a) He installed a flashing neon sign in the village shop.
   b) He began playing music in the shop.
   c) He started to stock men's magazines which sold well, even though they were positioned discreetly on the top shelf.

2. In the pilot series of *The Archers*, first broadcast in 1950, what was Brookfield Farm originally called?
   a) Lowfield
   b) Stoneberry
   c) Wimberton

3. Which bandleader opened the 1957 village fete?
   a) Acker Bilk
   b) Chris Barber
   c) Humphrey Lyttleton

4. To great acclaim and amusement, 'Cliff Pilchard' and 'Elvis Measley' performed long ago at the Ambridge village hall. Ned Larkin was 'Cliff Pilchard', but who was 'Elvis Measley'?
   a) Joe Grundy
   b) Tom Forrest
   c) Walter Gabriel

ANAGRAMS

Unscramble the following to reveal some fondly remembered characters.

1. GREET LARGE PINT

2. CHARGE CARER?

3. LARGE ABLER WIT

4. KIND 'N' REAL

5. RICHER ROADS

CRISS-CROSS: IN MEMORY

With this penultimate puzzle, here is a chance to remember and give thanks to some former characters. Find a place for them all by fitting them into the grid.

3-letter names
Dan
Nic
Sid
Tom

4-letter names
Jack
John
Mark
Phil

5-letter names
Betty
Doris
Grace

Julia
Laura
Nigel

6-letter names
Nelson
Walter

7-letter names
Heather
Siobhan

8-letter names
Caroline
Marjorie

ONE LAST RIDDLE

My first is in hot, never in cold,
And my second is found in a hill, not in a wold.
My third is seen in sea, never in the sky,
And my fourth is in blue but not in dye.
My fifth is seen in under, never in over,
And my sixth is in rambler but does not make a roamer.
My last is appropriately in last, never in first.
As this puzzle is last in the book,
Well done and rejoice in my whole.

ANSWERS

1. Anagrams
1 The Archers, 2 Ambridge,
3 Borchester, 4 Hollerton,
5 Felpersham

2. On Track
Glebe Cottage, Ambridge Hall,
Grey Gables, Home Farm and
(what a good place to end up!)
The Bull

3. Mystery Sudoku

O	R	I	N	L	A	G	F	M
N	L	M	R	F	G	O	A	I
F	A	G	I	O	M	N	R	L
I	F	N	L	A	O	R	M	G
R	M	O	F	G	N	L	I	A
A	G	L	M	I	R	F	N	O
M	O	R	A	N	L	I	G	F
G	I	A	O	R	F	M	L	N
L	N	F	G	M	I	A	O	R

4. Country Words
1b, 2b, 3a, 4c

5. Hidden Names
1 Ambridge has A LANdscape
I'll forever admire. 2 To sort
this out, I hAD A Meeting
place in mind and it's certainly

not The Bull. 3 This picture
taken at the last Ambridge
fete shows US HAving a really
good laugh. Great times.
Great memories. 4 Sometimes
I indulge in a littLE WIShful
thinking. Who doesn't?

6. Cryptogram
Never give your number to a
girl you are not interested in.

7. Word Search: The Archers

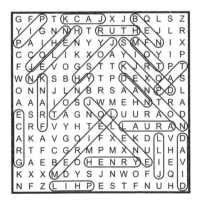

8. An Archers Riddle
Dairy

9. Trivia: Past and Present
1 Phoebe, 2 Shires, 3 Dylan
Nells, 4 Ferrets owned by Eddie
Grundy, 5 The Cat and Fiddle,

6 Joe Grundy, 7 A false bottom,
8 Eddie Grundy, 9 He was killed
in a tractor accident, 10 Ian
Craig and Adam Macy

10. Crossword
Across: 6 Clarrie, 7 David,
9 Matt, 10 Felpersham,
11 Reunites, 13 Incite, 15 Apse,
17 Heron, 18 Itch, 19 Cousin,
20 Blockade, 23 Welsh corgi,
26 Neil, 27 River, 28 The Bull
Down: 1 Bartenders, 2 Profit,
3 Bell, 4 Adhesion, 5 Eves,
6 Chase, 8 Drastic, 12 Shrub,
14 Chicken run, 16 Pioneer,
17 Handcart, 21 Oliver, 22
Drill, 24 Save, 25 Ruth

11. A Perplexing Poser
This was due to a time
difference between England and
Australia, where Meriel was
born. Jill received a phone call
from Kenton on Thursday 10
May to tell her of the birth of
his daughter in Australia at
6.20 a.m. on 11 May.

12. Wedding Bells
b, i, e, g, f, a, j, c, d, h

13. Ambridge Sudoku

D	B	E	I	M	G	A	R
A	M	G	R	E	D	I	B
M	I	A	D	R	E	B	G
B	E	R	G	D	I	M	A
E	A	D	B	I	R	G	M
R	G	I	M	B	A	E	D
G	D	B	E	A	M	R	I
I	R	M	A	G	B	D	E

14. What Could Possibly Go Wrong?
1c, 2c

15. Word Quest: Kenton
Nonet, tenon, token, tonne,
keno, knot, neon, none, note,
tone, eon, ken, net, non, not,
one, ten, toe, ton

16. Word Ladder
One possible solution: pig, pin,
pan, pay, say, sty

17. Coded Crossword

The name is 'Barwick Green', the familiar theme tune of *The Archers*.

18. Famous Moments

1 Bert Fry, 2 Fallon Rogers, 3 They played jurors at Helen's trial, 4 Colin Dexter, 5 Lynda Snell, 6 Sir Terry Wogan, 7 Anneka Rice, 8 Princess Margaret, 9 Duchess of Cornwall – she appeared in her role as the president of the National Osteoporosis Society, 10 Dame Judi Dench

19. Anagrams

1 Brian Aldridge, 2 Neil Carter, 3 Robert Snell, 4 Kate Madikane, 5 Tom Archer

20. Mystery Sudoku

O	T	I	M	N	E	B	C	H
M	B	E	C	T	H	I	O	N
H	N	C	B	I	O	T	M	E
C	H	N	O	M	I	E	B	T
B	O	T	E	H	N	C	I	M
I	E	M	T	C	B	H	N	O
T	M	H	I	O	C	N	E	B
N	I	B	H	E	M	O	T	C
E	C	O	N	B	T	M	H	I

21. What They Said

1c, 2b, 3b

22. Word Builder

Landscape

23. Name Jig

Elizabeth Pargetter, Oliver Sterling, Jennifer Aldridge, Eddie Grundy and Helen Archer

24. Country Words

1c, 2b, 3a, 4c

25. Mini Sudoku: Grundy

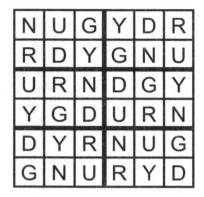

N	U	G	Y	D	R
R	D	Y	G	N	U
U	R	N	D	G	Y
Y	G	D	U	R	N
D	Y	R	N	U	G
G	N	U	R	Y	D

26. Take Your Pick
1b, 2b, 3a, 4a

27. Word Search:
The Countryside

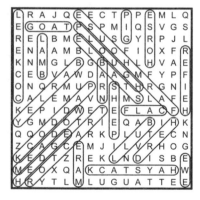

28. Cryptogram
The English winter – ending in
July, to recommence in August.

29. Maze

30. Trivia: Names
1 Oliver Sterling, 2 Doreen,
3 Fallon, 4 Pusscat, 5 Mark
Hebden's parents, 6 Joe Grundy,
7 Jess, 8 Leonie and Coriander,
9 Mungo, 10 The Stables

31. One from the Other
Home Farm and herbal leys

32. Criss-Cross:
Ambridge Residents

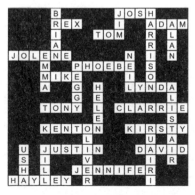

33. Follow the Leader
Neil Carter, Pip Archer,
Ed Grundy

34. Very Strange But True
c) The noise was from a loose
TV aerial tapping against a
drainpipe. The ghost hunter
never found anything.

35. Between the Lines
Villagers

36. Mystery Sudoku

O	T	S	V	E	K	L	I	C
E	K	C	T	L	I	S	O	V
V	L	I	S	C	O	E	K	T
K	O	L	C	V	E	I	T	S
I	V	E	K	T	S	C	L	O
S	C	T	O	I	L	K	V	E
L	I	V	E	S	T	O	C	K
T	S	K	L	O	C	V	E	I
C	E	O	I	K	V	T	S	L

37. True Diamonds
1 Home Farm, 2 Aldridge,
3 Harrison, 4 McCreary

38. A Farming Riddle
Cattle

39. Coded Crossword

The name is 'Underwoods', a
department store in Borchester.

40. Anagrams
1 Clarrie Grundy, 2 David
Archer, 3 Susan Carter,
4 Freddie Pargetter, 5 Roy Tucker

41. Crossword
Across: 1 Future, 4 Banana,
9 Beer, 10 Bridge Farm,
11 Isobar, 12 Musician,
13 Lakey Hill, 15 Will, 16 Soil,
17 Machinery, 22 Romantic,
23 Ruairi, 25 Blue cheese,
26 Blur, 27 Rehire, 28 Ethene
Down: 1 Freesia, 2 Throb,
3 Rebirth, 5 August, 6 Affection,
7 Airmail, 8 Dismal,
14 Elizabeth, 16 Spoiler,
18 Archer, 19 Harvest,
20 Reroute, 21 Etcher, 24 Abbie

42. Country Words
1a, 2c, 3a, 4b

43. Letter Drop
In good milk you should be able to taste the grass.

44. Take Your Pick
1a, 2c, 3b, 4c

45. Name Builder
Pemberton

46. Criss-Cross: Ambridge

47. Trivia: Times Past and Present
1 Kefir, 2 Nic Grundy, 3 Fence posts, 4 Lee, 5 Matt Crawford, 6 Brian Aldridge, 7 Strawberry, 8 Lower Loxley, 9 Eddie Grundy, 10 A meal for two at Grey Gables

48. Mystery Sudoku

I	E	R	T	M	S	A	P	N
P	M	A	N	I	E	T	S	R
T	N	S	R	A	P	E	M	I
S	P	E	A	R	M	I	N	T
M	A	N	I	P	T	S	R	E
R	T	I	E	S	N	P	A	M
A	I	P	M	E	R	N	T	S
E	R	T	S	N	A	M	I	P
N	S	M	P	T	I	R	E	A

Spearmint is the name of Alice's horse.

49. Cross Out
Joe Grundy

50. Hidden Names
1 After leaving schoOL, I VERy much fancied joining the military. 2 I hated being in a RUT. However, recent developments have opened up new possibilities. 3 In my business I have to looK AT Every aspect, including all the many regulations. 4 To lose that extra weight I guess I neED DIEtary advice on what best to avoid.

51. Cryptogram
Easy to get nothing wrong if you never do nothing in the first place.

52. Name Jig
Alistair Lloyd, Kathy Perks, Hayley Tucker, Josh Archer, Lynda Snell

53. Word Search: Animals

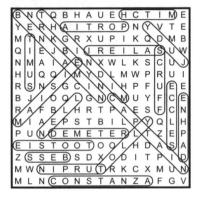

54. Word Builder
Spiritual

55. Mini Sudoku: Silage

G	I	S	L	E	A
L	A	E	I	G	S
S	G	L	A	I	E
I	E	A	G	S	L
A	S	G	E	L	I
E	L	I	S	A	G

56. What Could Possibly Go Wrong?
1c, 2b

57. Archers Hide and Seek

```
A R H A E A C S E R S H A C H
R R C R E S R A C R A R C H S
A S H R C A H S E R S E H S A
C R C R S C R A H A S H R E R
E S A R E C A C E R C E H R A
A R H R C E H R E S R E S R S
S R R R C C A C H C S E R C H
A E S H E C R S E A R S H E A
C S H R S A C S S C S E H R C
A S R A E C R S E A E A C E A
R R C R E C R X C E R S E H R S
A A H A S C A R H A H E C A E
S A S C E H R S E E S E H S R
A R E A S C A H E A R A R A A
C A R A E C H S E R S S H C A
```

58. Anagrams
1 Alistair Lloyd, 2 Kenton Archer, 3 Lewis Carmichael, 4 Lily Pargetter, 5 Rex Fairbrother.

59. True or False?
1 True. 2 False. He was an accountant. 3 False. There was a Janet Fisher who was vicar – Ambridge was one of the first parishes to have a female incumbent. 4 False. 5 True. 6 False. 7 True. This was actually the result of an April Fool's joke. Debbie had told Eddie that some sovereigns stolen from Netherbourne Hall were hidden among the gravestones. Eddie duly went in search of them. 8 True. 9 True.

60. Criss-Cross

61. Letter Drop
I could whip something up with this venison.

62. Country Words
1c, 2a, 3a, 4c

63. Word Ladder
One possible solution: cows, mows, mods, mode, mole, mile, milk

64. A Picture Poser
Borchester Crown Court (where Helen faced trial): boar – chest – stir – crown – court

65. Coded Crossword

The Orangery is a café at Lower Loxley.

66. Hidden Charms
1 Cress, 2 Hutch, 3 Order, 4 Tawny, 5 Elder – the words in the shaded squares read 'rural scene'

67. Word Search: Names

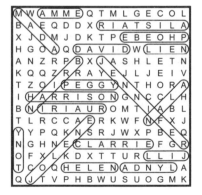

68. Trivia: Times Gone By
1 A badger, 2 Stefan had seen
Rob's actions in blocking a
culvert on the Berrow Estate,
an action that led to the terrible
flood, 3 Six months, 4 Mark
Hebden, 5 Alan Titchmarsh,
6 Walter Gabriel, 7 Penny
Hassett, 8 Jolene and Sid,
9 Susan, 10 Northumberland

69. Interesting Puzzle
1e, 2j, 3l, 4b, 5a, 6h, 7i, 8c, 9k,
10g, 11d, 12f

70. Word Builder
Community

71. Word Search: Field Names

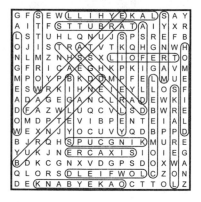

**72. What Could Possibly
Go Wrong?**
1b – villagers thought the
culprits may have been the
Loxley Barrett Morris Men, 2a

73. Acrostics
1 Apollo, 2 Manger, 3 Belong,
4 Retina, 5 Intern, 6 Delphi,
7 Garlic, 8 Eccles – and the
shaded squares spell 'Ambridge
Organics'

74. Mini Sudoku: Veg Box

E	G	B	V	X	O
V	O	X	E	G	B
G	B	E	O	V	X
O	X	V	G	B	E
B	V	O	X	E	G
X	E	G	B	O	V

75. Hidden Names
1 I like playing in AmbridGE
OR GEtting out in the open
countryside. 2 This lady has
aspirations of one day being
seeN AT A SHAreholders'
meeting. 3 If it's a case of being
more frugAL, I CErtainly can
cut down on the food bill. 4
My new housekeeping systEM
MAkes sense, seeing as how we
have to economise now.

76. Mind the Gap
Hollerton. Hollerton Junction
is Ambridge's nearest railway
station, which is why it would
be wise to 'mind the gap'.

77. Cryptogram
'If it doesn't hurt a little when you lose, there's no point in playing.' Alistair was talking about gambling.

78. Word Search: Love Stories

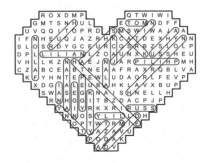

79. Anagrams
1 Ambridge Hall, 2 The Dower House, 3 Willow Cottage, 4 The Stables, 5 The Vicarage

80. Mystery Sudoku

81. Take Your Pick
1b, 2c, 3c

82. Word Ladder
One possible solution: meet, melt, belt, bell, Bull

83. Criss-Cross

84. Country Words
1a, 2b, 3a, 4c

85. Hidden Delight
Placebo, nearest, patient, reacted, weekend, illegal, amateur. The shaded word is 'cricket'.

86. Name Jig
Alan Franks, Lily Pargetter, Carol Tregorran, Brenda Tucker, Jolene Archer

87. Cryptogram
One thing about the Archer family, things never stop happening, do they?

88. Crossword

Across: 1 Suburb, 4 Freda Fry,
9 Active, 10 Aldridge,
12 Optional, 13 Offend,
15 Ambridge Hall, 18 Matt
Crawford, 23 Lilian,
24 Titanium, 26 Ed Grundy,
27 Whiten, 28 Entreaty,
29 Crocus
Down: 1 Seasonal, 2 Bathtubs,
3 Ravioli, 5 Role, 6 Direful,
7 Fodder, 8 Yields, 11 Targets,
14 Chervil, 16 Holistic,
17 Oddments, 19 As a rule,
20 Weather, 21 Fleece, 22 Flight,
25 Edit

89. Letter Drop

A good man is hard to find.
A good hairdresser, next
to impossible.

90. Mini Sudoku: Quinoa

N	Q	A	U	O	I
U	O	I	N	A	Q
I	A	N	Q	U	O
Q	U	O	A	I	N
A	I	Q	O	N	U
O	N	U	I	Q	A

91. Word Search: Dogs

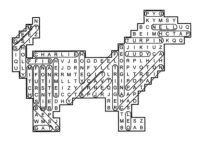

92. Anagrams

1 Hayley Tucker, 2 Justin Elliott,
3 Natasha Archer, 4 Christopher
Carter, 5 Lilian Bellamy

93. Name Builder

Titchener

94. On Track

Helen, Lilian, Brian, Clarrie,
Oliver, Susan, Robert, Lynda,
Neil

95. Mystery Sudoku

C	P	M	R	U	E	D	H	O
U	R	H	C	O	D	E	P	M
D	O	E	P	H	M	U	C	R
E	D	P	O	R	U	C	M	H
H	U	R	E	M	C	P	O	D
M	C	O	H	D	P	R	E	U
R	E	D	M	P	O	H	U	C
P	M	U	D	C	H	O	R	E
O	H	C	U	E	R	M	D	P

96. Trivia: Past and Present
1 Jennifer, 2 Alice Aldridge, 3 Heydon Berrow, 4 Ellis, 5 Montbéliarde, 6 Jazzer, 7 Leonard, 8 Sepsis, 9 He was a Spice Girls stripogram, 10 Hannah Riley

97. Cryptogram
There's nothing worse than slack pants, loose boots and a cap that doesn't fit.

98. Criss-Cross

99. Acrostics
1 Bridge, 2 Excess, 3 Rabbit, 4 Raffia, 5 Object, 6 Wobble. The name 'Berrow Estate' appears in the shaded squares.

100. Hidden Names
1 In the next sceNE, I'Ll be able to show my acting prowess. 2 As there's not much time, we'll need TO BYpass the queue somehow. 3 It's mum's sponge caKE I RAther like, especially if it has lots of jam. 4 If someone sendS US ANother order, we will beat last month's sales figures.

101. Coded Crossword

F	L		J	Z		D	T		V		I
A	C	A	D	E	M	E		E	G	O	T	I	S	M

The organisation is Damara Capital.

102. Word Ladder
One possible solution: hunt, hint, mint, mind, mild, mill, bill, ball

103. Letter Drop
'Eddie Grundy! What have you done this time?' Despairing words that Clarrie has said on many an occasion.

104. Country Words
1a, 2c, 3b, 4a

105. The Mysterious X
1 Honest, 2 Famous, 3 Psyche, 4 Ankles, 5 Secret, 6 Remedy. The name formed in the X is none other than Hayley Tucker.

106. True or False?
1 True, 2 False, 3 True, 4 False, 5 False, 6 True, 7 False, 8 True, 9 True, 10 False

107. Word Builder
Pheasants

108. Anagrams
1 Debbie Aldridge, 2 Brenda Tucker, 3 Usha Franks, 4 Pat Archer, 5 Alice Carter

109. Word Quest: Oliver
Liver, lover, oiler, olive, oriel, viler, voile, evil, live, lore, love, over, rile, rive, roil, role, rove, veil, vile, viol, vole, ire, lei, lie, oil, ore, rev, roe, vie, vol

110. Cryptogram
If you can plant your foot upon nine daisies then spring has come.

111. Criss-Cross: The Countryside

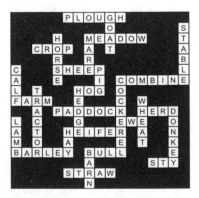

112. A Perplexing Poser
The path

113. Mystery Sudoku

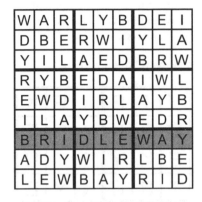

114. Coded Crossword

The tradition is Stir up Sunday.

115. Name Jig
Clarrie Grundy, Susan Carter, Adam Macy, Kenton Archer, Mike Tucker

116. Word Builder
Milk quota

117. Cryptogram
Some of the biggest arguments between our writers are over t he characters.

118. Mini Sudoku: Turkey

Y	T	R	U	E	K
U	E	K	Y	R	T
E	K	Y	R	T	U
T	R	U	K	Y	E
K	Y	T	E	U	R
R	U	E	T	K	Y

119. Cross Out
GM crops

120. Fitting Words
Tractor

121. Trivia: Past & Present
1 Lilian Bellamy, 2 David Archer, 3 A portable toilet, 4 Grace, 5 That they were in a relationship. Lily actually used Meredith as cover for her affair with Russ, 6 Buying, renovating and selling farm machinery, 7 Eddie Grundy, 8 Clarrie Grundy, 9 a) Tom Archer, b) Justin and Lilian

122. Country Words
1c, 2a, 3b, 4a

123. Follow the Leader
Roy Tucker, Ed Grundy, Kathy Perks

124. Wedding Bells
h, c, a, j, e, b, f, g, i, d

125. Strange But True
c). The reason was that the product did not exist. It was an April Fool's joke by Pat and Tony – Lipoflora is an anagram of 'April Fool'!

126. Word Search: Vegetables

127. Take Your Pick
1b, 2a, 3c, 4b

128. Word Ladder
One possible solution: home, tome, tame, fame, fare, farm

129. Between the Lines
Omnibus

130. Anagrams
1 Elizabeth Pargetter, 2 Dan Hebden Lloyd, 3 Susan Carter, 4 Debbie Aldridge, 5 David Archer

131. Mystery Sudoku

R	U	T	N	L	V	E	A	C
N	C	L	R	E	A	T	V	U
A	V	E	U	T	C	N	R	L
C	R	U	A	N	E	L	T	V
L	A	N	T	V	R	C	U	E
T	E	V	C	U	L	A	N	R
V	N	A	E	C	U	R	L	T
E	L	R	V	A	T	U	C	N
U	T	C	L	R	N	V	E	A

132. On Track
Bridge Farm, Arkwright Hall, The Stables, St Stephen's Church

133. A Perplexing Poser
The letter 'e'

134. What They Said
1b, 2c, 3b

135. Hidden Delights
River Am

136. Anagrams
1 Emma Grundy, 2 Pip Archer, 3 Shula Hebden Lloyd, 4 Lewis Carmichael, 5 Brian Aldridge

137. Cross Out
Stockman

138. An Ambridge Riddle
Poach

139. Cryptogram
'I have only ever put myself at the disposal of the community, from motives of pure altruism.' These are, of course, the words of Lynda Snell.

140. Mini Sudoku: Yogurt

141. Criss-Cross: The Archer Family

142. Country Words
1a, 2a, 3c, 4b

143. Word Ladder
One possible solution: farm, form, fort, foot, soot, shot, shop

144. Hidden Resource
1 Mumps, 2 Ideal, 3 Lorry, 4 Koala, 5 Idiom, 6 Nexus, 7 Glory. The words in the shaded squares spell 'milking parlour'.

145. What Happened Next?
b) Phil switched the labels back to ensure that all was as it should be.

146. Word Builder
Husbandry

147. Anagrams
1 Dan Hebden Lloyd, 2 Anna Tregorran, 3 Mia Grundy, 4 Pat Archer, 5 Ruairi Donovan

148. Word Quest: Justin
Just, snit, stun, suit, unit, jus, jut, nit, nut, sin, sit, sun, tin, tis, tun

149. Down Word
Alpaca, oldest, farmer, impart, bandit, assess. The shaded word is 'llamas'.

150. Name Jig
Roy Tucker, Neil Carter, Ruth Archer, Freddie Pargetter, Lilian Bellamy

151. Letter Drop
'Just get on with the job in hand is my motto.'

152. Mini Sudoku: Pigsty

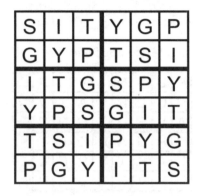

153. Trivia: Names
1 Ursula, 2 Gideon Robert, 3 Lynda Snell, 4 Jolene Rogers, 5 Vancouver, 6 Miranda, 7 Hilda Ogden is a bad-tempered cat given to Peggy Woolley by Fabrice, her hairdresser, 8 Norman Painting, who played the character Phil Archer, 9 Marjorie Antrobus, 10 Ed Grundy's sheep

154. Criss-Cross: Ambridge Residents

155. Cryptogram
When it said, 'Buy one, get one free,' I don't think it referred to shoes.

156. What Could Possibly Go Wrong?
1c Lynda had baked the cake following a seventeenth-century recipe, which made the crust unbreakable. 2a With its brittle skin and rotted flesh, gas built up within the marrow, causing the unfortunate consequence.

157. Word Ladder
One possible solution: Lily, lilt, list, lust, rust, Russ

158. Hidden Names
1 Although some of my plans have involved quite an upheavAL, I CErtainly think everything has worked out for the best. 2 He was unusually annoyed and outspoKEN TONight, but quickly calmed down. 3 I like to follow a systEM, MAinly because that way I know I can get more done. 4 I think it is important to be enthusiastiC. A ROLe model for others can work wonders.

159. Word Search: Weather

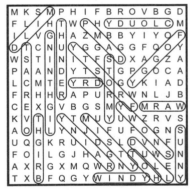

160. Strange But True
d)

161. Word Builder
Scarecrow

162. Mystery Sudoku

O	S	E	D	B	M	R	G	A
B	A	D	G	E	R	S	O	M
G	R	M	O	A	S	D	E	B
A	E	B	M	R	O	G	S	D
M	D	G	E	S	A	O	B	R
S	O	R	B	D	G	A	M	E
R	M	A	S	G	B	E	D	O
D	G	O	A	M	E	B	R	S
E	B	S	R	O	D	M	A	G

163. Take Your Pick
1b, 2c, 3b, 4c

164. Word Search: Well-Known Names

165. A Picture Poser
Karate lessons: car – Ra – tea – less – suns

166. Pigs and Cows
1 pigeon, 2 pigtail, 3 pigment, 4 pig-headed, 5 piggyback, 6 piggy bank, 7 pigeonhole, 8 cowslip, 9 coward, 10 cower

167. Anagrams
1 Phoebe Aldridge, 2 Oliver Sterling, 3 Ian Craig, 4 Alice Carter, 5 Brenda Tucker

168. Cryptogram
'What does a girl have to do to get a drink round here?' – Lilian Bellamy

169. Criss-Cross: Dogs

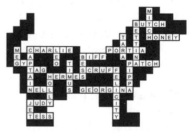

170. Mini Sudoku: Plough

P	G	U	H	O	L
O	L	H	U	P	G
L	H	O	P	G	U
G	U	P	L	H	O
U	P	G	O	L	H
H	O	L	G	U	P

171. A Perplexing Poser
Notable, not able, no table.
The sentence is therefore: After Lynda's notable production, she was not able to serve canapés as she had no table.

172. Country Words
1b, 2b, 3a, 4c

173. Hidden Names
1 The sample jars of fruit JAM I Expected from Ambridge Organics have just arrived.
2 I believe the decision of the board was JUST. I Now need signatures in order for the scheme to go ahead.
3 I am hoping HE LENds his full support to the new breed.
4 After the promotion, the number of lamB ENquiries doubled, much to my relief.

174. Acrostics
1 Ditch, 2 Apple, 3 Inner, 4 Round, 5 Yolks. The shaded squares spell out 'dairy herds'.

175. Follow the Leader
Ian Craig, Jim Lloyd, David Archer

176. Take Your Pick
1a, 2b, 3b, 4c

177. Anagrams
1 Dan Archer, 2 Nelson Gabriel, 3 Ned Larkin, 4 Tom Forrest, 5 Sid Perks

178. Cryptogram
Come to the point and get there quick, shilly-shallying makes me sick.

179. Who Did What?
1g, 2h, 3a, 4f, 5i, 6b, 7j, 8c, 9e, 10d

180. Word Search: Ponies and Horses

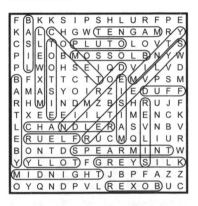

181. Criss-Cross: Issues

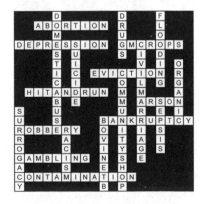

182. Word Ladder
One possible solution: seed, shed, shod, shop, chop, crop

183. Mini Sudoku: Justin

T	J	I	N	U	S
S	U	N	J	T	I
N	S	U	I	J	T
I	T	J	U	S	N
U	N	T	S	I	J
J	I	S	T	N	U

184. Coded Crossword

The annual event is Apple Day, which takes place in October.

185. Name Jig
Peggy Woolley, Robert Snell, Harrison Burns, Emma Grundy, Brian Aldridge

186. What They Said
1a, 2a, 3b

187. Mystery Sudoku

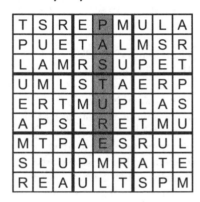

188. Word Search: Unsung Characters

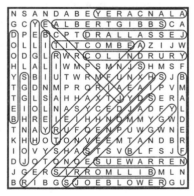

189. Anagrams
1 Phil Archer, 2 Marjorie Antrobus, 3 Nigel Pargetter, 4 Nelson Gabriel, 5 Caroline Sterling

190. Country Words
1a, 2c, 3c, 4a

191. Mini Sudoku: Stable

L	B	T	E	S	A
S	A	E	L	B	T
A	S	L	B	T	E
T	E	B	A	L	S
B	T	A	S	E	L
E	L	S	T	A	B

192. Between the Lines
Freda Fry

193. Word Builder
Farmhouse

194. Cryptogram
Like a rusty nail being driven through the bottom of a cocoa tin.

195. Coded Crossword

The name is 'Midnight'. This was the horse that Grace tried to rescue in the stable fire.

196. Mini Sudoku: Larkin

I	R	K	A	L	N
N	A	L	R	K	I
K	I	A	N	R	L
L	N	R	I	A	K
A	K	N	L	I	R
R	L	I	K	N	A

197. Take Your Pick
1a, 2c, 3c, 4c

198. Anagrams
1 Nigel Pargetter, 2 Grace Archer, 3 Walter Gabriel, 4 Ned Larkin, 5 Doris Archer

199. Criss-Cross: In Memory

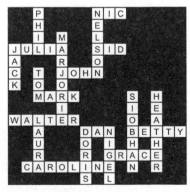

200. One Last Riddle
The Bull

ACKNOWLEDGEMENTS

In compiling this book I have been greatly assisted by my wife Ros, a long-time *Archers* fan who is blessed with a remarkably good memory – not only of things relating to *The Archers* but pretty much everything else! Thank you, Ros.

I am grateful too for the support of Richard and Emily, my son and daughter, for trying out some of the puzzles. David Finnerty and Barbara Smith have also given much appreciated input, as has Pam Pickett with her excellent knowledge of *The Archers* and useful suggestions.

As always, the team at Summersdale have been wonderful to work with and I would particularly like to thank Robert Drew, my editor, Claire Plimmer for her support, and Beth Miller for her expertise.

Thanks too to the BBC and all who have made and make *The Archers* the joy that it is. And last, but not least, I would like to thank you the reader for your interest in this puzzle book and hope that it has – and will continue to give you – a lot of fun.